1934

1.87

Elements

of

Farm Management

Elements
of
Farm Management

by

John A. Hopkins, Ph. D.

Associate Professor of Agricultural Economics
Iowa State College

NEW YORK

PRENTICE-HALL, INC.

1936

PRINTED IN THE UNITED STATES OF AMERICA

Preface

THE PURPOSE of this book is to set forth some of the basic principles of production economics in a simple and realistic manner. *Elements of Farm Management* does not attempt to cover the entire field of production economics, but confines itself to a small number of fundamental principles. The principle of increasing and diminishing returns, the closely related principle of comparative advantage, and the principle of substitution are of primary importance. Their ramifications extend throughout the organization and management of the farm business.

In a course in farm management the student should acquire a thorough grasp of these underlying tendencies or principles. He should see that the successful operation of a farm is not simply a matter of adopting approved practices and following empirical rules. Rather he should realize that there are many choices among the possible combinations of the factors of production. No techniques or practices are beyond question, and the most satisfactory practice under one set of conditions may not be economical under another.

The farm is treated as a going concern—as it appears to the student who is living on a farm while he is studying farm management. The elementary student is not likely to be greatly interested in principles as such. Consequently this book is not organized, primarily, around the abstract principles. Instead, they are presented as inter-

v

est in them would naturally arise in practical problems of farm operation.

The main discussion has been confined to farm management, and it is assumed that books of reference will be available on the related subjects of marketing, methods of crop and livestock production, and so on. However, some of the relationships of the farm organization to the external business world are pointed out in Section VIII. This includes the relationship between farm management and marketing, and between farm management and problems of financing. This section is intended to develop leads to these subjects rather than deal with them in an exhaustive manner.

There is a close connection between farm management and farm records. Instead of treating them in a separate section, appropriate records are introduced in connection with whatever part of the farm may be under discussion. Thus, in discussing the crop plans, records of soil treatment and crop yields are suggested and described. In dealing with livestock enterprises, records of feed consumption and of livestock production are discussed as tools to profitable management. Considerable attention is given to the method of budgeting as a means of choosing enterprises and of obtaining balance within the farm business.

In planning the organization of a farm, and in checking up on its operation, it is necessary to have some definite standards of the amounts of feed, labor, and so on, used per unit of output. Such data usually have to be obtained from widely scattered sources. An effort has, therefore, been made to bring together here such information on some of the more important farm enterprises. This is not intended simply as factual information but as material to aid in application of the principles of farm organization and management.

To accompany this text a set of suggested Problems and Activities has been developed, largely by Professor H. M. Byram, of the Department of Vocational Education of Michigan State College. Acknowledgment is due to Professor Byram not only for the preparation of these problems, but also for suggesting numerous changes in the text which should make it more useful in the classroom.

Acknowledgment is also due to Professor L. G. Allbaugh, of the Iowa Agricultural Extension Service, and to several others for making a critical examination of the manuscript and suggesting various improvements. I am indebted to Professor W. G. Murray for assistance in organizing the chapter on Financing the Farm Business, and to Professor G. S. Shepherd for assistance with the chapter on Marketing the Farm's Produce.

Above all I am indebted to my wife, whose careful editing of the entire book has greatly simplified its language and made it more readable.

JOHN A. HOPKINS

Ames, Iowa
August, 1936

Contents

Part I

GENERAL CONSIDERATIONS

Part II

ORGANIZING THE FARM: BASIC PRINCIPLES

ix

PART III

THE CROP SYSTEM

PART VIII

EXTERNAL RELATIONSHIPS OF THE FARM
BUSINESS

Illustrations

PART I

GENERAL CONSIDERATIONS

CHAPTER I

Economic Activity and Choosing an Occupation

The Problem: Shall I choose farming as a means of earning a living? How do the returns from farming compare with those of other professions? How can I succeed as a farmer?

Choosing an Occupation

When a young man chooses a business or profession, he is making one of the most important decisions of his life. After he has begun his training for one particular profession, it is difficult to change to some other line of work, and such a change becomes even more difficult and expensive after he has really got started in his profession.

If a profession or an industry becomes overcrowded, it may take years for it to become profitable again; thus a poor choice may put a man at a disadvantage for the greater part of his life. Naturally one cannot prophesy with any degree of certainty the condition of an industry or profession twenty or thirty years hence, but in order to avoid costly errors one should choose his vocation as thoughtfully and sensibly as possible. After obtaining all the information he can about the various vocational fields, he should weigh carefully the advantages and disadvantages of the different vocations in which he is interested.

Economic Activity

What should be considered in choosing an occupation? Usually the strongest influence on one's choice is that of economic returns. By economic returns we mean the *income received*. This income is mostly money which will be converted into goods and services to be either consumed or added to one's possessions. The term *economic activity* means *one's work or effort in providing goods or services for which people are willing to pay*. It includes, of course, similar services which one performs for himself.

Robinson Crusoe obtained his living directly. He gathered or raised his own food. He made his own clothing, built his own shelter, and in his spare time entertained himself by writing his diary, beautifying his surroundings, or watching the antics of the animals around him. But Crusoes do not exist in our modern society. Under the present economic organization each person can obtain with less effort more of the things he needs if he specializes his business activity. The farmer raises wheat, but it is the miller who grinds it into flour and the baker who makes the flour into bread for the final consumer.

What is the economic objective of the farmer, or of any other member of our modern economic society? Each is anxious to operate his business profitably, that is, to get a maximum return from his resources. The farmer's resources are his *labor*, his *capital*, and his *land*. These are sometimes called *factors of production*. In order to insure a maximum return from these resources, the product should possess *a value as much in excess as possible of the value of the production factors consumed* in raising that product.

Value

The term *value* is one we shall use frequently. Just what do we mean when we say, for example, that a bushel of wheat has a greater value than a bushel of corn? We mean that in return for our bushel of wheat we can get more of the other things we want; more sugar, potatoes, clothing, or whatever we need. In other words, *value is the power which one article gives us to purchase, in exchange, other goods or services.* Value should not be confused with *price*, which is simply one limited form of value.

Price is value in terms of money. Prices may change without a change in the value of anything but money. If wheat is selling for $1 per bushel, oats for 50 cents per bushel, and sugar for 5 cents per pound, we can say that the value of a bushel of wheat is equal to that of two bushels of oats or twenty pounds of sugar. If the price of wheat rises to $1.50, oats to 75 cents, and sugar to 7½ cents, all the *prices* will have increased by 50 per cent, but the values, except in terms of money, will be unchanged. A bushel of wheat will still have a value equal to that of two bushels of oats or 20 pounds of sugar.

A Broad View of Economy

Profitable production calls for the practice of economy. This means getting the greatest return from the full use of resources. It does not mean, as is commonly supposed, merely a sparing use of what we have. Economy is much more than that; it is the most advantageous use of all our resources and faculties.

There is an economy of money-making, but the mere accumulating of money is not one's sole objective in life.

There are many satisfactions whose value cannot be estimated in terms of money. What price should one put on the enjoyment of a sunset, on a concert of his favorite music, on the chance to go to a good school, or on good medical and hospital facilities? Which is the wiser, the person who plans merely for the largest possible money in-

Courtesy Wallace's Farmer-Homestead

Fig. 1.—Such a home may be one of the satisfactions of farm life.

come or the one who plans for the most satisfying and well-rounded life?

The money income should be regarded in its proper place—as a means of procuring whatever desirable things can be obtained with money. We must not forget, however, that there are many desirable things which can be obtained directly and without purchase from others. In order to enjoy them, however, it may be necessary to give up the chance to produce some salable product. The true practice of economy consists in choosing those things we

TABLE I

PURCHASING POWER, IN 1913 DOLLARS,[a] OF THE ENTIRE
REALIZED INCOME DRAWN BY INDIVIDUALS FROM THE
VARIOUS INDUSTRIES

(Millions of 1913 Dollars[b])

Data from National Bureau of Economic Research
"The National Income and Its Purchasing Power," Table XVI

Year	All Industries	Agri- culture	Manu- facturing	Banking	Mer- cantile	Govern- ment
1909	31,300	5,139	5,808	357	3,922	1,645
1910	32,380	5,239	6,411	402	3,869	1,732
1911	32,920	4,948	6,455	423	4,169	1,824
1912	34,656	5,376	6,970	437	4,123	1,896
1913	35,756	5,133	7,332	453	4,488	1,981
1914	35,250	5,063	6,821	447	4,700	2,060
1915	36,636	5,591	7,185	451	4,775	2,124
1916	39,559	6,032	9,326	434	4,897	2,067
1917	40,242	6,643	9,789	396	5,055	2,353
1918	40,150	7,015	9,705	372	4,604	4,030
1919	38,017	6,644	9,084	359	4,667	3,423
1920	37,573	5,540	9,618	379	4,432	2,607
1921	36,710	4,459	7,519	477	4,859	3,161
1922	40,565	4,974	8,434	560	5,337	3,480
1923	45,164	5,538	10,013	591	6,530	3,416
1924	46,758	5,681	9,688	609	6,701	3,483
1925	48,412	5,795	9,826	634	7,117	3,542
1926	50,421*	5,163*		671	7,347*	
1927	52,892*	5,539*			7,666*	
1928	54,022*	5,456*			7,993*	

[a] "1913 Dollars" is an abbreviation for the phrase "dollars having purchasing power equivalent to that which they had in 1913."

[b] Computed from the corresponding items in Table XIV in "The National Income and Its Distribution" by dividing the various sub-items for each industry by the appropriate price indices recorded in Table VII of the same book.

* Preliminary estimate.

want most and, incidentally, in giving up the things we
want less.

The Farmer's Income

What sort of income can the farmer expect, and what
has been the trend of agricultural income as compared to
incomes from other industries?

From Table I we see that, during the whole period from
1909 to 1928, the income of the farm population changed
very little, whereas the income of some other groups increased rapidly. Income from manufacturing industries,
banking, mercantile activities, and governmental activities
including public schools almost doubled between 1909 and
1928. However this does not mean that the per capita income in those industries doubled, for most of the increase
in population was going into those fields. Nevertheless,
the per capita increase in city income was large and greatly
exceeded the increase in the farmer's income.

TABLE I-A

BUREAU OF COMMERCE ESTIMATES OF
NATIONAL INCOME[a]

Income Produced by Industrial Divisions (Millions of Dollars)

Year	Total	Agriculture	Manufacturing	Finance[b]	Trade	Government
1929	81,034	7,159	19,308	8,219	10,955	6,805
1930	67,917	5,555	14,072	7,113	9,131	7,043
1931	53,584	3,601	9,526	5,702	7,372	7,189
1932	39,545	2,335	5,623	4,360	5,254	7,148
1933	41,889	3,300	7,797	3,677	5,772	6,741
1934	48,561	4,451	9,791	3,859	6,340	6,992

[a] From U. S. Department of Commerce: "The National Income Produced 1929-'34,"
by Robert R. Nathan, Nov. 1935. Data not directly comparable with those in Table I.
[b] Includes banking, insurance, and real estate excluding individual holdings.

TABLE II

NET VALUE, AT AVERAGE PRICES OF 1909-1913, OF
TOTAL FARM PRODUCTS PER ACRE, PER FARMER,
AND PER CAPITA

Data from National Bureau of Economic Research
"The National Income and Its Purchasing Power," Table XCIII

Year	Acres of Crop Harvested[a] (Thousands)	Number of Farmers[a] (Thousands)	VALUE OF NET PRODUCE AT AVERAGE PRICES OF 1909-1913 (DOLLARS)			
			Total (Millions)	Per Acre Harvested	Per Farmer	Per Capita
1909	316,028	6,289	5,629	17.81	895.05	62.19
1910	328,655	6,307	5,738	17.46	909.78	62.08
1911	334,993	6,322	5,934	17.71	938.63	63.24
1912	332,085	6,336	6,221	18.73	981.85	65.31
1913	336,755	6,346	5,953	17.68	938.07	61.30
1914	337,160	6,353	6,069	18.00	955.30	61.32
1915	346,698	6,359	6,620	19.09	1,041.04	65.94
1916	346,411	6,365	6,225	17.97	978.00	61.16
1917	354,309	6,369	5,814	16.41	912.86	56.32
1918	363,346	6,374	6,207	17.08	973.80	59.47
1919	366,063	6,378	6,340	17.32	994.04	60.38
1920	361,136	6,381	5,983	16.57	937.63	56.22
1921	360,176	6,387	6,051	16.80	947.39	55.84
1922	363,515	6,271	6,129	16.86	977.36	55.85
1923	364,265	6,297	6,346	17.42	1,007.78	56.93
1924	358,530	6,344	6,570	18.32	1,035.62	57.90
1925	363,515	6,317	6,409	17.63	1,014.56	55.73
1926	364,690	6,200*	6,604*	18.11*	1,065.22*	56.71*
1927	363,598	6,124*	6,647*	18.28*	1,085.34*	56.34*
1928	367,469	6,102*	6,760*	18.40*	1,107.83*	56.60*

[a] Based upon Census of Agriculture and U. S. Department of Agriculture reports.
* Preliminary estimate.

Comparison of Farm and City Incomes

We are on safe ground when we compare the *relative* changes in income of these different industrial groups, particularly when we use such carefully prepared figures as those of the National Bureau of Economic Research. But we need to be very careful in making comparisons in actual dollars between farm and other income for any particular year. We cannot make direct comparisons between *money income* of farmers and money income of people in cities. Living conditions differ in country and city, and the farmer receives or produces many things for which the city dweller has to pay cash.

First, there is the dwelling. We seldom think of house rent as part of the farm income. On both rented and owned farms the house is generally considered as more or less "thrown in" along with the land. Since the house is a

TABLE II-A

NET VALUE AT AVERAGE PRICES OF 1909-1913 OF
TOTAL FARM PRODUCTS

Year	Acres of Crops Harvested (Thousands)	Number of Farmers (Thousands)	VALUE OF NET PRODUCE AT AVERAGE PRICES OF 1909-1913 (DOLLARS)			
			Total[a] (Millions)	Per Acre Harvested	Per Farmer	Per Capita
1929	357,827	6,029	$4,903	$13.70	$813	$40.10
1930	359,927	6,289	4,409	12.25	701	35.75
1931	350,672	6,393	4,139	11.80	647	33.50
1932	354,671	6,497	3,592	10.13	553	28.78
1933	324,070	6,601	4,714	14.55	714	37.50
1934	286,512	6,705	4,946	17.26	738	39.12

[a] Derived from data in Table I-A, Column 2, by dividing by index of prices of agricultural products on 1909-1913 base. Data not directly comparable with those in Table II.

part of the general farm layout, it is not possible to make a distinction between the house and the rest of the farm income. The city dweller, however, must either invest in a house in addition to his business investments or else spend part of his income for rent.

Another important item of income received directly from the farm is home-raised foods. This includes dairy produce, poultry, eggs, butchered meats, vegetables, fruits, and so on. Kirkpatrick found, in his study of 2,886 white farm families in 11 states in 1922-1924, that the average value of food consumed per family was $659, of which $441 was raised on the farm.[1] Another large item was fuel, of which Kirkpatrick found an average of $43 worth, or approximately half, provided by the farm.

Out of an average value of $1,598 for family living, goods and services worth $684 were furnished by the farm, according to Kirkpatrick's study. In other words a city dweller would need a money income of at least $1,684 to be as well off as a farmer with a cash income of $1,000. Nor is this all. Kirkpatrick states that the farm produce was usually valued at rates for which it would have sold, and these are, of course, lower than prices which the city dweller would have had to pay for such produce. Our city dweller would probably need an amount closer to $2,000 to obtain the living available to the farmer with a net cash income of $1,000. Therefore figures which seem to show that farmers have a lower income than city people are apt to be misleading.

Advantages of the City

On the other hand, city people can procure at a mod-

[1] Kirkpatrick, Ellis Lore, *The Farmer's Standard of Living*, New York, Appleton-Century, 1929.

erate price many things which the farm family has difficulty in obtaining at all. These include city light service and water supply, libraries, a wide variety of amusements, and often better schools. Expert medical care and hospital facilities may be had promptly in the city; in the country these may be difficult to secure without serious delay.

Fortunately, improved roads and communication services are rapidly making many of the city facilities available to the farm family as well. The farm is no longer isolated. While most of the advantages of city living are becoming available to the farmer, the city dweller finds many of the pleasures of country life, which we are apt to take for granted, either impossible to attain or prohibitive in price.

Opportunities for Financial Success in Farming

While the average cash income of farmers is a rather small figure, there is, however, a wide variation in farm incomes. Many farmers have incomes that the majority of storekeepers and other business men would be glad to receive.

Table III shows the variation in net income of 632 Iowa farmers in 1929. Their average net income was $2,649. This amount is the sum left over after all operating expenses were deducted from the gross income. It represents earnings on the farmer's capital, rent on his land, if he owns his farm, and wages for labor performed by himself and members of his family.

Approximately half of these 632 farmers had net incomes between $1,000 and $3,000. There were a few whose net incomes, even in this favorable year, were a minus quantity. At the other extreme were 68 with net incomes of more than $5,000, and one with more than $10,000.

Similar variations occurred in other years. In 1932 there were heavy losses, but some of the more successful farmers in the group earned satisfactory incomes. The upper 10 percent had net incomes of over $1,000, whereas

TABLE III

VARIATION IN NET INCOME ON IOWA FARMS

Year	1929	1932	1933
Number of Farms	632	570	471
Average Net Farm Income	$2,649	$ −55	$2,265
Net Income:			
$8,000 or over	6	...	3
7,000 to $7,999	12	...	3
6,000 to 6,999	17	1	6
5,000 to 5,999	33	...	9
4,000 to 4,999	53	...	16
3,000 to 3,999	94	6	72
2,000 to 2,999	170	4	139
1,000 to 1,999	159	45	153
0 to 999	66	219	67
− 1 to −1,000	16	229	3
−1,001 to −2,000	3	47	...
−2,001 to −3,000	1	14	...
−3,001 or less	2	5	...

the least successful 10 percent were in the red by $1,300 or more. In 1933 improving farm prices resulted in the upper 10 percent's having net incomes of over $4,000, while the lower 10 percent had net incomes of less than $500.

This sort of variation is typical of farm accounting data. In farming, as in any other industry, income varies with the ability and training of the individual. It varies also with the years' climatic condition, its rainfall, tempera-

ture, and similar factors, and with the size of the business
and the price movements of farm crops. It is true that
great fortunes are not made by farm operation. Farming
is not a business which lends itself readily to successful
operation of large units. However, this should not be considered a serious drawback. In other industries the percentage of men who make large fortunes is also small.
Enormous fortunes are spectacular and attract much attention, but they are not nearly so numerous as many people believe.

What Are the Requirements for Success in Farming?

How do farmers achieve success? Is it luck, or the result of training and effort? What are the characteristics
of successful farmers? In general they are alert and always on the lookout for ways of improving their farming
methods. They keep abreast of the times by contacts
with the county agent and with teachers of agriculture and
the agricultural colleges. They also discuss their problems frequently with their wide-awake neighbors.

The successful farmer is the one who is intelligent and
industrious, who has a knowledge of up-to-date agricultural techniques, and who has the ability to use businesslike methods.

An important study of personal characteristics and conditions which make for success in farming was carried on
in Minnesota.[2] It is interesting to learn from the data
collected the farmers' own opinions on the relative importance of the fifteen factors studied. Seventy-two farmers
rated these factors in the following order of importance:

[2] Pond, George A., and Wilcox, Walter W., "A Study of the Human
Factor in Farm Management," *Journal of Farm Economics*, Vol. XIV,
July 1932.

1. Farm experience.
2. Wife's co-operation.
3. Ambition to achieve success.
4. Liking for farm work.
4. Getting work done on time.
6. Hard work.
7. County agent's help.
8. Production management.
9. Farm papers.
10. Father's having been a good farmer.
11. School training.
12. Buying and selling ability.
13. Use of outlook information.
14. Ability to handle labor.
15. Children's help.

TABLE IV

OPERATOR'S LABOR EARNINGS AS RELATED TO TEST ON
TECHNICAL INFORMATION

Score	Number of Men	Average Operator's Labor Earnings
Under 60	12	$ 841
60 to 69	20	867
70 to 79	38	937
80 to 89	47	1,262
90 and over	19	1,443

According to this study, there was no connection between the amount of property inherited and the labor earnings. Twenty-one farmers who inherited half or more of their property made average labor earnings of $558, whereas thirty-eight who inherited less earned $1,176. The remainder of the group, who inherited no property, made the best showing with average labor earnings of $1,213. The method of selecting the farmers interviewed may partly account for this result. These farmers

were keepers of farm records, and we naturally expect to
find a greater percentage of record keepers among men
who have made themselves successful than among persons
who have inherited farms.

The Farmer's Economic Problem

We said that the farmer's economic problem is to obtain
the greatest possible return from his resources.   How can
he do this?   The solution to the problem has two phases:
(1) the efficient operation of the farm itself, and (2) pro-
vision for the most satisfactory and profitable arrangements with persons or businesses outside the farm.

Adjustment to the physical and economic conditions
around us is not so simple as we might think.   Costs differ with climate and soil, and freight rates vary with location.   In order to plan a profitable farm we must, therefore, make a thorough study of economic and natural conditions.   This phase of our problem will be considered
further in the next chapter when we take up types of
farming.   The farmer of today is very dependent upon
other persons and other industries.   There is no longer
among farmers such a thing as self-sufficiency, and the
more we study the matter the less desirable self-sufficiency appears.

How can we achieve the most efficient operation of the
farm itself?   The answer to this question is the special
field of farm management.   We must select crop and livestock enterprises, and then organize them into an efficient
system.   We must plan a budget for smooth financial
operation of the farm.   After the proper plans are made,
we then devote our attention to the actual operation of the
farm, seeing that crops are attended to at the right times
and that hired labor is always profitably employed.   Farm

records should be kept to provide a check on the plan or budget, and to enable us to know the condition of the farm business at any time.

Leaving the farm itself, we must consider problems of marketing, transportation, farm credit, government policy on tariff, taxation and such matters. If the farmer cannot sell or use his crops profitably, he will not be able to realize any profit on his efficient production. Therefore, the farmer must find out what types of products are wanted by the buying public. He must select and produce those things for which people are willing to pay satisfactory prices and which can be grown on his particular farm.

Many farmers blame the marketing system for not giving them a satisfactory price, whereas the real trouble is that they are producing something for which there is no longer a sufficient demand. At the present time the farmer who continues to raise a large acreage of timothy seed is in the same position a manufacturer would be if he insisted upon making celluloid collars—and he makes about the same profit.

References

App, Frank, *Farm Economics, Management and Distribution,* Lippincott, Philadelphia, 1924, Chapter I.

Carver, T. N., *Principles of Rural Economics,* Ginn, Boston, 1911, Chapter I.

Holmes, C. L., *Economics of Farm Organization and Management,* Heath, Boston, 1928, Chapter I.

Kirkpatrick, Ellis Lore, *The Farmer's Standard of Living,* Appleton-Century, New York, 1929.

Overton, M. H., and Robertson, L. S., *Profitable Farm Management and Marketing,* Lippincott, Philadelphia, 1929, Chapter I.

Pond, George A., and Wilcox, Walter W., "A Study of the

Human Factor in Farm Management," *Journal of Farm Economics*, Vol. XIV, July 1932.

Warren, G. F., *Farm Management*, Macmillan, New York, 1916, Chapter I.

Arkansas Bulletin 271: "Farm Standards of Living in Faulkner County, Arkansas," by J. T. McCormick, 1932.

Indiana Bulletin 369: "The Human Factor in the Management of Indiana Farms," by W. W. Wilcox and L. G. Lloyd, 1932.

Illinois Bulletin 372: "Living Expenditures of a Selected Group of Illinois Farm and Small Town Families, 1929-30," by Ruth C. Freeman and M. Attie Souder, 1931.

Iowa Bulletin 281: "Value of Family Living on Iowa Farms," by Elizabeth E. Hoyt, 1931.

Minnesota Bulletin 255: "Incomes and Expenditures of Minnesota Farm and City Families, 1927-28," by Carle C. Zimmerman, 1929.

Minnesota Bulletin 279: "Relation of the Farm Home to the Farm Business," by Lucy A. Studley, 1931.

CHAPTER II

Types of Farming

The Problem: How can I know what type of farming to choose? What are the general forces that determine the location of the various types of farming areas?

Natural Influences Help Determine Type of Farm

Natural forces are most important in determining the types of farming in any locality. Let us see how natural conditions affect our choice of farm enterprises.

Climate. Climate, soil, and topography are the main natural forces that determine our success in raising certain crops in various localities. Under climate we include length of growing season, temperature, and amount of sunshine and rainfall. Oats and potatoes are crops which grow well in a relatively cool climate with a short growing season. Corn requires a warmer growing season than oats, and grows best in rather moist air with the temperature between 80 and 90 degrees Fahrenheit. Cotton also needs a moist, warm climate but requires a longer growing season, usually 200 days or more.

Among the forage crops, alfalfa does well in a relatively dry climate, whereas most of the grasses grow better if they have more moisture. But for all these crops clear, sunny days are needed for harvest. Cloudy, rainy days during harvest increase the cost of harvesting and result in a poorer quality of hay. Each crop does best under a cer-

19

tain combination of climatic conditions rather than under a continuation of the same conditions for the whole season.

Soil. The type and condition of soil are important in determining which crops to raise. We know, for example, that we cannot raise alfalfa on an acid soil, where potatoes would thrive. Kentucky blue grass grows best with abundant lime in the soil, whereas Canada blue grass will grow in spite of acid soil. Wheat grows best in a soil that has a relatively close texture and contains considerable clay, but sweet potatoes and watermelons require a sandy soil. Corn needs a mellow, loamy soil; however, oats will grow too rank and lodge if the soil is too rich. On each definite soil type we find there are certain crops that do well, others that grow only moderately well, and still others that can hardly be raised.

Topography. Topography means the general contour of the land—whether it is hilly or level. Because contour determines the kind of machinery that can be used and the rate of soil erosion, it affects considerably our choice of crop. For example, a corn field on level land may be cultivated and harvested with large machines, while their use on a steep hillside would be impossible. On level land, labor requirements and other costs will be considerably less than on steep, hilly land. Therefore successful farmers generally use the rough land for pasture or for crops which do not require cultivation. However, if climatic conditions are good and the soil is fertile, fairly steep hillsides may be cultivated intensively—for vineyards, commercial orchards, and so on.

Natural conditions may make it actually impossible to produce certain crops in a given locality. Suppose, however, that each of two crops may be grown fairly well in a certain community but that one of them will return more for the labor and capital than the other. How would you decide which crop to produce? What economic principles are involved? In choosing your crop, how can you apply these principles to the circumstances and the natural conditions on your farm?

Economic Determinants of Type of Farming

People often remark that some crop, such as sugar, which is purchased from other parts of the country or from some foreign country could be produced at home. They conclude, then, that since it *could* be produced, it *should* be produced at home in order to save freight or to make the home community "self-sufficing."

The practical man generally answers this statement by saying that it "does not pay" to produce at home most of the articles shipped in. This, however, is not a complete answer. What he really means is that there are other crops in the production of which the home locality has a greater advantage. If we sell the things we produce and with the money received buy goods at *relatively* lower costs in other countries, we can obtain these goods with less effort than if we try to produce them directly.

For example, a corn belt farmer has been buying each year a carload of 20 feeder calves, costing $700. A neighbor suggests that he should raise his own feeders and save this expense. The farmer begins to figure which would be the more profitable procedure. He finds that, if he were to keep 20 cows and raise their calves to the age of those he has been buying, it would require about 50 acres of pasture for cows and calves, 15 acres for hay, and 5 for corn—70 acres in all. In addition, a certain amount of labor and capital would be required. Now the farmer begins to wonder if raising these calves is the most prof-

itable use he can make of this land. If he were to put
the land into the prevailing rotation (corn-corn-oats-
hay), he would get, in yields per acre, about 40 bushels
of corn, 38 bushels of oats, and 1⅓ tons of hay. Each
year there would be about 35 acres in corn, 17½ acres in
oats, and 17½ acres in hay, with yields of 1,400 bushels
of corn, 655 bushels of oats, and 23 tons of hay. At 65
cents for corn, 35 cents for oats, and $12 for hay, these
crops would be worth $1,415 for sale or for feed. The
farmer then estimates that expenses other than the use
of the land would be: $300 for keeping the beef cows, or
$600 for raising the crops. After deducting these ex-
penses, he finds that the 70 acres would bring a net return
of $400 if the calves were raised, or $815 if the crops were
grown. The farmer thus proves that his first plan is the
better one, since he can buy more calves from the proceeds derived from the use of the same land by raising
crops and selling them.

Comparative, not absolute, costs are the guide. We
must remember that the principle we are discussing con-
cerns *comparative* and not *absolute* costs. That is, the
competition is between different goods in the same locality, and not between absolute costs for the same commodity in different localities.

A community often finds it advantageous to buy from
abroad a commodity which can be produced more cheaply at home—in terms of absolute costs. Let us suppose
that a week's work in Community A would produce 100
bushels of corn or 60 bushels of wheat; whereas in Community B a week's work would produce 50 bushels of
corn or 40 bushels of wheat. Even though the wheat is
produced at a lower absolute cost in Community A, it
will be advantageous for that community to buy its

wheat from Community B. How can we show this?

In Community A, corn and wheat will tend to exchange in a ratio of 100 bushels of corn for 60 bushels of wheat. In Community B, the ratio of exchange will tend to be 100 bushels of corn for 80 bushels of wheat. If the farmers in Community A need wheat, they can exchange 100 bushels of corn, raised by one week's work, for only 60 bushels of home-raised wheat. However, if they take their corn to Community B, they will find that 100 bushels of corn will exchange for more than 60 bushels of wheat. It might buy as much as 80 bushels of wheat, although at that rate it would be just as advantageous for the Community B farmers to raise corn as wheat. If the exchange ratio were about 100 bushels of corn for 70 bushels of wheat, the exchange would be profitable to both sides.

Of course, in the preceding argument we have not considered freight and handling charges, but so long as these are not great enough to equalize the difference in relative cost of the two commodities, the two areas will find it to their advantage to specialize in their more profitable crop.

Law of Comparative Advantage

The principle known as the *law of comparative advantage* may be stated briefly as follows: *The producers of each locality tend to use their resources in the production of the goods with the lowest relative costs. With the proceeds from these goods they purchase, for their own use, goods produced under greater advantage elsewhere.*

Note that the principle is stated as a *tendency* and not as a condition which is always true. Various factors may interfere with the natural functioning of this tendency.

Cheap methods of transporting a crop from one locality to the other may not have been developed; or, as in the case of foreign trade, one or both nations might see fit, for military or other reasons, to interfere with trade by tariffs or embargoes. This principle, like other economic principles, merely describes the arrangement which, if followed, would be to the greatest advantage of both communities.

Regional Competition of Enterprises

If two crops can both be grown in the same area, what determines which one will win out? Value, of course, for one thing. If the value of one of these crops gives it an advantage over the other, it will tend to crowd out the less profitable one.

Suppose that one of these crops is cotton, which can be grown only in a limited area, the southern states in this country, and that the other is corn, which can be grown in the cotton belt and in other areas as well. In such a case *the crop which is adapted to the more limited conditions will tend to have its choice of area while the other will tend to be produced elsewhere.* The production of cotton is more limited by climate and other conditions than is the production of corn. Therefore in regions where cotton grows well, farmers make more money by raising cotton than they do by producing corn.

Changing values shift production areas. Cotton *can* be raised somewhat north of the present cotton belt. What determines where the cotton belt ends and the corn belt begins? As we go north we find that, because of cooler climate and a shorter growing season, the returns from cotton growing decline. Then we come to an area where the returns from growing cotton are the same as those from raising corn. North of this area it is possible for a small cotton crop to be raised, but in most years corn has yielded a greater return from the land with the same amount of labor. If the price of cotton should rise or that of corn should fall, the cotton belt would expand into this territory where the two crops now compete.

Which crop is more profitable depends partly on the price received and partly on the cost of production. A satisfactory mechanical cotton picker would lower the cost of producing cotton and would, therefore, do much to expand its production. But if more cotton were raised, its price would be lowered. In the long run the expansion would be limited by this decline in price.

Transportation costs help determine localization of enterprises. Have you ever heard of a farmer who, having shipped a carload of produce, found that he had nothing left over after paying freight and commission charges? He may blame either the railroads or the marketing system, or both. It may be true that the marketing system is inefficiently organized and that railroad rates are high, but the real reason for such an occurrence is probably one of the following two: either too much of that particular crop is being produced; or the farmer has chosen to produce something which cannot be marketed economically from his locality.

Why are milk and green vegetables usually produced near large cities, whereas grains and meat animals are raised at greater distances from population centers? Let us suppose that at a certain market hay is selling for $15 per ton; wheat for 90 cents per bushel, or $30 per ton; and wool for 30 cents per pound, or $600 per ton. Assume that freight charges are $2 per ton per 100 miles. How far could each of these products be shipped before the farmer would have to pay out, for example, half the market price for freight charges? On a strictly mileage basis (which is, however, not precisely the way freight rates are fixed) the hay could be shipped 375 miles, the wheat 750 miles, and the wool 30,000 miles (more than the distance around the world).

High freight makes for concentration of product. Transportation costs are important in determining whether a crop product is to be marketed as such, or whether it is to be converted into a more concentrated livestock product. A farmer living in the eastern part of the dairy belt might find it profitable to sell baled hay, but if he lived in a western state he could probably get more for the hay if he first fed it to cattle or sheep.

To illustrate, a farmer now living in central Iowa finds that the freight to Chicago on corn is $18\frac{1}{2}$ cents per hundred pounds and on hogs is 39 cents per hundred pounds. Let us assume that he can produce 100 pounds of live hogs with 10 bushels of corn. The freight on the 10 bushels, or 560 pounds, of corn would amount to $1.04. He can save 65 cents by using the corn for feed and selling the hogs, if the market price of the hogs promises to be as high as that of corn.

Less advantage in feeding bulky crops near markets. On the other hand, a farmer living in Illinois finds that the freight to Chicago is 12 cents on corn and 19 cents on hogs. The freight on the 10 bushels of corn is 67 cents and on the 100 pounds of hog 19 cents. In this locality, therefore, the advantage in feeding the corn to the hogs is only 48 cents as compared with the 65 cents from central Iowa.

As we go east toward the consuming centers, the advantage of feeding the corn becomes smaller. Event-

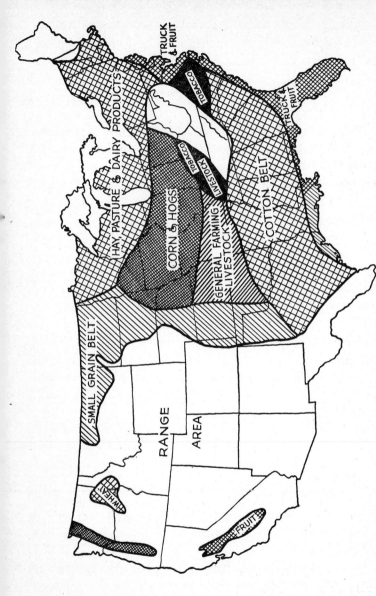

Fig. 2.—Principal types of farming areas in the United States.

ually we reach a place where it pays to market the grain as corn instead of hogs.   In eastern markets we find that the prices of such commodities as wheat, corn, hogs, and beef cattle, which are shipped toward the eastern part of the country, tend to equal the prices in western markets plus freight and handling charges.   In choosing his principal enterprises the farmer should study prices and transportation costs carefully in order to discover the advantages of his particular locality.   He should also consider the possibility of converting his crops into more concentrated products, which may be marketed more economically.

Perishability of product and the producing areas. Another consideration in studying transportation costs is the relative perishability of the product.   Transportation costs, as well as losses from spoilage, are greater for products which deteriorate rapidly.   Therefore fluid milk and green vegetables are produced usually in areas near large cities.   Every improvement in transportation methods, such as refrigeration, tends to increase the areas where these products may be grown profitably. Fruits, vegetables, and milk are now shipped long distances to market, but this is more true of the less perishable fruits and out-of-season products.

In spite of the advantages which cotton production has in the southern states, we find that considerable corn is raised there.   Although hog production has the advantage in the corn belt, a large number of hogs are raised in the eastern part of the country.   Are these farmers unwise, or would they find too great a specialization unprofitable?   Where is the point of greatest advantage between specialization and diversification? This subject will be considered in the next chapter.

Types of Farming in the United States

How have economic principles caused specialization in the United States? Let us find on a map of this country the crops that are grown in each section. (See Fig. 2.) Except for products which are perishable or bulky, we see that our main crops are produced mostly in areas where natural and economic conditions are favorable.

Photo *J. C. Allen & Son*

Fig. 3.—A dairy farm.

Dairy belt. In Fig. 2, the area in which most of the hay and dairy products are produced is a belt extending from southern New England westward into southern Minnesota. In this area the growing season is too short and too cool for corn to grow well and ripen properly. Rainfall is adequate and well distributed over the growing season; pasture is excellent, and good crops of hay can be raised. The dairy can use this hay and pasture to advantage, and does not require so much grain as is necessary for raising hogs or beef cattle.

Small grain belt. West of the Missouri River we find the wheat or small grain belt, extending west as far as Montana and from the Canadian boundary south to Texas. From central Nebraska north, spring wheat is raised; winter wheat is raised to the south. Wheat is the most productive grain crop in this semiarid area and is more profitable than grazing. Wherever large-sized machinery can be used, wheat is the principal crop. The development of the *combine* has extended the wheat belt farther west into semiarid regions where it seldom was profitable to raise the crop before.

In Washington and Oregon there is a mixed spring and winter wheat area. The rainfall in this region is insufficient for most other crops, but the soil and temperature are favorable to wheat production.

In the east there is a large area, extending from Pennsylvania to the Missouri River, where winter wheat is raised in rotation with corn and other crops. Here corn generally has the advantage over wheat, but since the soil and climate are favorable to wheat also, it fits into the rotation as a nurse crop for hay or pasture. In some dairy regions an important function of wheat is to furnish bedding for the dairy cows.

Thus we see that there are various combinations of natural and economic conditions which make wheat the principal crop in some sections and a secondary crop in others. In no case is the importance of the crop due either to natural or to economic conditions alone.

Corn belt. South of the dairy belt we find (see Fig. 2) an area where the growing season is longer and temperature and rainfall are sufficient to ripen corn. The soil of most of this area is so rich and mellow that excellent yields are secured. The rolling land found in a large part of the corn belt provides adequate drainage and at the same time permits the use of large-capacity machinery.

Courtesy International Harvester Co.

Fig. 4.—Extensive wheat production requires but little labor per acre of land.

The corn area of greatest concentration is a belt, 150 to 200 miles wide, extending from northeastern Nebraska eastward to central Ohio. Corn is, however, widely raised and is grown from central Minnesota to the Gulf of Mexico and from the Atlantic seaboard to central Colorado. Nevertheless, the six principal states of the corn belt—Ohio, Indiana, Illinois, Iowa, Nebraska, and Missouri—furnish approximately half the corn produced in this country. Outside the corn area the combination of climate and soil is generally less advantageous, although there are small areas, such as southeastern Pennsylvania, where corn is a very important crop.

North of the corn belt the season is too short to mature the crop properly, and to the west the rainfall is inadequate. In the south, cotton is more profitable as the main crop.

Courtesy Alabama Agricultural Extension Service
Fig. 5.—A cotton farm.

The areas of concentrated production of hogs are practically the same as those of corn. The hog is a convenient and economical means of converting grain into a product which has less bulk and greater value per pound and which can be shipped to market with a saving of freight. Corn can also be fed to beef cattle, but they require in addition a considerable amount of roughage which the usual crop combinations on the best corn land

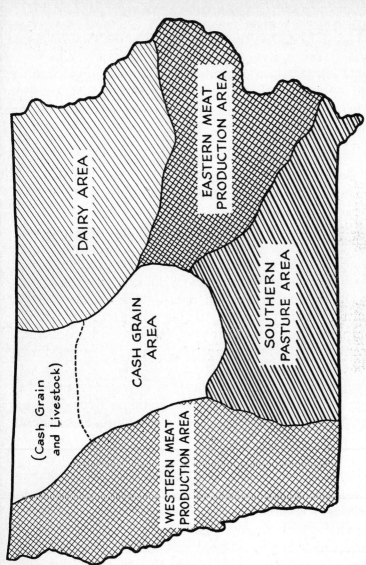

Fig. 6.—Types of farming in Iowa.

33

do not provide. More hay and pasture would have to be raised, and these would lower the value of the crops. In the hillier sections of the corn belt, beef cattle are raised on the land used for pasture and are fattened on corn from the more level parts of the farms. In areas where there is but little untillable land, feeder cattle are frequently purchased from western markets and fattened on corn after being pastured on cornstalks.

Cotton belt. South of the 37th parallel is the area known as the cotton belt, which has three fairly distinct areas of concentration. The first is the Piedmont region of South Carolina and Georgia. The second is the alluvial soil along the Mississippi. The third region, which has become much more important during the past twenty years, is in Texas and Oklahoma.

Other crop production areas. The four large agricultural areas named in the preceding text are not the only areas of specialized production. We have already mentioned the intensive vegetable-producing areas near the large cities. There are a number of important apple-producing areas. Then, of course, there are the citrus areas of California and Florida. Even in these specialized areas, however, secondary crops, such as oats in the corn belt, are raised.

Specialized production does not always result from natural or economic advantages. Sometimes it is the result of a *lack* of advantage for a more profitable product. For example, most of the land from the 100th meridian west to the Pacific states is used for grazing, not because it is especially good for grazing but because there is not sufficient rainfall to enable other crops to be raised without irrigation.

Variations within type areas. Within each major type of area there are many variations. This is illustrated by Fig. 6, which shows that several sub-types may exist within the boundaries of a single state.

Iowa is, of course, one of the principal states of the corn belt; yet in the northeastern part of the state, dairying is the main farm enterprise. The rough land and ample rainfall of that section make excellent pasture land. In the southern part of the state, also, there is rolling land but the pastures are apt to dry up in summer. Also the oat crop, important in the dairy ration, does not grow so well here as in the cooler northern part of the state. Much of the southern area is kept in pasture and used for producing beef cattle, which may be sold as feeders or fed on corn from other parts of the state.

In the north central part of the state is a section devoted chiefly to raising corn and oats. The land is level and very fertile. Corn yields are heavy, and large-capacity machinery is used. Most of the farms are large, and more corn is raised than is needed for the hog enterprises. Much of the land is too productive to be left in pasture, except for some sweet clover or alfalfa, and consequently few cattle are raised. Since not much livestock is raised, large amounts of corn and oats are sold, especially from rented farms.

In the western part of the state there is fertile soil but rolling to rough land. Corn yields well, and there is considerable hog feeding. The rough land provides a large acreage of pasture which is utilized by beef-raising or steer-feeding enterprises. Similar land in the eastern part of the state provides another corn-hog-and-beef area.

As shown by the above illustration, even in one state there is sufficient variation in natural conditions to provide several distinct types of areas. In fact there is often sufficient variation between neighboring farms to make their organization quite different. We may find a hog farm on one side of the road, and perhaps a steer-feeding farm on the other, both of them doing equally well.

References

Black, J. D., *Production Economics*, Holt, New York, 1926, Chapters V, VII.

Gray, L. C., *Introduction to Agricultural Economics*, Macmillan, New York, 1924, Chapter II.

Holmes, C. L., *Economics of Farm Organization and Management*, Heath, Boston, 1928, Chapter IV.

Taylor, H. C., *Outlines of Agricultural Economics*, Macmillan, New York, 1925, Chapter V.

Iowa Bulletin 256: "Types of Farming in Iowa," by C. L. Holmes, 1928.

Kansas Bulletin 251: "Types of Farming in Kansas," by J. A. Hodges, F. F. Elliott, and W. E. Grimes, 1930.

Kentucky Bulletin 357: "Types of Farming in Kentucky," by Bruce Poundstone and Walter J. Roth, 1935.

Massachusetts Bulletin 244: "Type-of-Farming Areas in Massachusetts," by Ronald L. Mighell and Marion Brown, 1928.

Michigan Bulletin 206: "Types of Farming in Michigan," by E. B. Hill, F. T. Riddell, and F. F. Elliott, 1930.

Minnesota Bulletin 257: "Types of Farming in Minnesota," by F. F. Garey, 1929.

Nebraska Bulletin 244: "Types of Farming in Nebraska," by Harold Hedges and F. F. Elliott, 1930.

Oklahoma Bulletin 181: "Types of Farming in Oklahoma," by J. O. Ellsworth and F. F. Elliott, 1929.

U. S. Department of Commerce, Bureau of Census, 15th Census of the U. S. Census of Agriculture: "Types of Farming in the United States," by F. F. Elliott, 1933.

U. S. Department of Agriculture, Farmers Bulletin 1289: "Distribution of Types of Farming in the United States," by W. J. Spillman, 1923.

CHAPTER III

Specialization or Diversification?

The Problem: In order to obtain a maximum profit, should a farmer specialize in that enterprise to which he and the farm are best suited? Or, should his first concern be the business stability and safety that he could obtain through diversification?

Specialization or Diversification?

A young farmer decides that his farm is best suited to wheat and accordingly plants a large part of his land in this crop. But the season proves a bad one for wheat: the spring is dry, the harvest time wet. The price falls, and the farmer suffers a heavy financial loss. The county agent tells him that he should have diversified his farm so that the loss of a single crop would not have affected him so seriously. The farmer replies that he was following the principle of comparative advantage—that, after one finds out for what crop his farm is best suited, he should grow as much of it as possible.

Is there a conflict here between two principles? What course should be followed?

What Is Diversification?

Just what do we mean by *specialization* and *diversification?* We are apt to use the terms so loosely in ordinary conversation that all we really mean is *more*

37

specialization, or *less*. Specialization may refer to the production of a small group of products in a certain area; for example, corn, hogs, and beef cattle in Iowa. The term may refer to the production of a small group of products, or even of a single product, by an individual. It may mean only one step in the production of an article; for example, when a farmer fattens cattle that have been raised by someone else. In industry it may refer to specialization, by occupations or tasks, among individual workers; for example, the laborer in a shoe factory who cuts out a single piece of leather or sews a single seam.

For our purpose we may best consider specialization as the production of only one commodity for market so that the farmer depends on a *single* source of income. By diversification we shall mean that several things are produced for market so that the farmer depends on *several* sources of income.

Obviously there are very few farms which are completely specialized in the sense just indicated. Neither are there many on which numerous sources of income are of equal importance. Under the term *income*, we should, of course, include *income in kind*, that is, goods used directly in the household as well as return from goods sold. Most farms are so organized that they receive the main part of their income, not from a single product, but from a small group of closely related products which may center around a single enterprise. This type of organization is sometimes described as semi-specialized farming.

Advantages of specialization. Our study of the principle of comparative advantage indicates that a certain piece of land should grow the crop which is best suited to it economically, and thus obtain the largest possible returns from that land. This is one of the arguments for specialization.

Specialization allows a man to become more skillful at doing a few things and hence increases his efficiency. The man who spends all or most of his time working in an orchard is more proficient at this work than is the man who has to go from plowing to milking, from pitching hay to picking fruit. However, in most types of farming the opportunities for gaining great skill by continuous work at the same job are very limited. Even in raising a single crop a man will do many different kinds of work during the season. Still it is true that the more enterprises there are on the farm, the less opportunity the farmer has to develop real skill and efficiency.

Another advantage of specialization is that it allows the farmer to use his capital more economically. The wheat farmer needs machinery only for raising wheat. If he has a large acreage, he can obtain efficient large-capacity machinery at a moderate outlay of capital per acre of wheat. If he is raising wheat, corn, and hay, the acreage of each may not be large enough to justify the use of large-capacity machines. Since each of the three crops requires special equipment, a greater total investment is necessary.

Specialization makes farm management much easier. The fewer enterprises there are in the farm organization, the fewer things the farmer has to keep at his fingertips if he is to manage efficiently and profitably. If there are too many enterprises, he is apt either to concentrate his attention on one or two enterprises and neglect the others or else to jump from one problem to another until none receives the attention it needs.

Advantages of diversification. Does specialization use to best advantage all the factors of production? Consider labor, for example. If a farmer raises wheat only, he will be extremely busy at two seasons of the year—when the crop is being planted and again when it is harvested and threshed. During the rest of the year there is little to do except a few odd jobs about the buildings. Also, horses and tractors, as well as other equipment which might be used for additional crops, are idle much of the time.

The wheat farmer could raise a considerable acreage of corn without hiring much, if any, more labor, since the two crops do not have to be cultivated or harvested at the same time. Then if he were to add a few dairy cows, he might still find it unnecessary to hire another man. Of course, milking and caring for the cows would make longer working days in the crop season, but it is possible to plan the dairying so that it requires the most labor during the winter season. Thus the farmer could have two more sources of income with little, if any, more expense for labor.

As far as the use of the land is concerned, heavy yields cannot be obtained year after year from the same crop on the same field. If the fertility of the soil is to be maintained or built up, there must be a satisfactory rotation of crops. A mere change in crops does not, of course, mean a satisfactory rotation. When the requirements of the different crops are not considered, rotation runs down the soil instead of maintaining its fertility or building it up.

Diversification reduces risk. Another possible advantage of diversification is that it reduces the business risk. There are two phases of risk: crop failure because of unfavorable weather, and loss due to unfavorable prices. In both cases, insurance against loss by diversification is only partial.

Losses may be reduced by selecting a rotation of crops which make most of their growth during different parts of the season. For example, in 1934 a serious drought early in the growing season practically wiped out the oat crop in parts of the corn belt. Corn suffered less injury because of the rains which began early in July. Although most of the farmers in this area usually raise both oats and corn, they suffered some loss on both crops. In a section with only one crop, however, as in some parts of the wheat belt, such a severe drought would either have reduced the farm income to practically nothing or would have had little or no effect, depending on when it occurred.

Let us suppose that the farmer who raises only wheat has a complete failure from drought one year out of every four, and the farmer who raises four different crops has a 25 percent failure each year. The latter will be injured less by his losses. Of course it is possible, when only one crop is raised, to lay up a reserve for years of crop failure, but most farmers neglect to do this.

The risk from unfavorable prices is reduced by diversification, but not so much as most people think. There are year-to-year variations in price from the corresponding fluctuation in size of each crop. Over the entire country an advance in price may offset a decrease in the yield. An individual farmer may have a poor crop when the crop for the country as a whole is large. He then not only has a small crop to market but gets a low price for it. Therefore he would be likely to gain by having more than one crop to sell.

Unfortunately, diversification of cash crops does not

safeguard against the most serious type of price decline.
In major business depressions all farm prices decline together. During such periods the problem is to try to
select those crops which fall more slowly during the decline, and then to shift to those which respond most quickly during the recovery. For instance, prices of dairy
products have generally fallen more slowly than grain
prices during the decline, but grain prices usually rise
more rapidly during recovery. Naturally a farmer cannot make a complete change in his organization, but even
a small amount of flexibility is worth working for.

Proper Combination of Enterprises

We can see now that the problem of organizing a farm
involves more than merely having a variety of enterprises.
The most important question is which *combination* of enterprises should be used, and what should be the relative
size of each. Even though corn is ordinarily the most
profitable crop of the corn belt, still it is possible to raise
so much corn on a farm that the result is not the greatest
return for effort expended. The farmer might find it
more profitable to raise less corn, and to feed some hogs
and raise more oats and some hay for a few cattle.

Does this violate the principle of comparative advantage? Not at all. Rather it gives us a fuller understanding of that principle. *The greatest comparative advantage usually results from a combination of enterprises
rather than from any single one.* These enterprises must
be selected with the idea of getting a satisfactory return
from the land for a long period of years, not just for a
single year. They must also make the best possible use
of labor and capital, as well as of the land itself.

In order to select the right enterprises for a certain farm, we must first study the relationships that may exist between them.

Competing enterprises. There may be a definite conflict or competition between certain enterprises—for example, the competition between crops for the land on which they are raised. If the acreage of one crop is to be increased, there must be a corresponding reduction in the acreage of some other crop.

There is also competition for labor. The labor requirements of a large acreage of soy beans will very likely conflict with the needs of the corn crop. In the cotton belt there is labor competition between the corn and the cotton crops. Some crops compete for labor during certain periods but not in others. The first cutting of alfalfa conflicts with the cultivation of corn. Winter wheat follows corn in the rotation and the two crops compete for the land during one period in the fall.

In planning his farm organization, the farmer should try *to select for his main sources of income those crops or livestock enterprises which promise to yield the largest net income for the use of his resources.* Net income here refers to returns from the whole organization, not from individual enterprises. The main enterprises, those about which the rest of the farm business is to be built, will naturally be selected first. In the western part of the corn belt there may be a choice between wheat and corn, and in the southern part between corn and cotton or tobacco. Perhaps some of each of the two competing crops will be grown, although usually one or two crops definitely dominate the farm organization.

Choice of enterprise should be based on net income. In deciding on the main enterprises, the only satisfactory basis for choice is the net income promised by the farm as a whole if it is organized around the proposed enterprise. Various other bases of choice have been suggested but have shown serious limitations. Choosing the crop that offers the largest net return per acre is not always satisfactory, because the labor requirements of such a crop are often so high as to make prohibitive to most farmers the profitable growing of such a crop, except in very small amounts.

Another basis for choice that is sometimes suggested is the return which the enterprise promises per hour of labor. But that involves also the question of how many hours of employment per year this crop would provide. A corn crop which may not give a very high rate of return per hour spent on it, can still be selected as the main crop because the necessary labor is distributed over a fairly long period of time and also because the corn can be used to support livestock enterprises which use labor profitably during the winter.

Should we try to raise those crops whose money costs of production are lowest in comparison with their market prices? Even if we could satisfactorily compute costs per unit, there would still remain the problem of how many pounds or bushels we could produce. In most cases, however, the money cost per unit cannot really be determined. How will the farmer who is raising sheep separate the cost of the wool from that of the lambs raised? If he is raising corn and also feeds the stalks, how can he determine the cost of one apart from the other except by purely arbitrary means? The existence of these joint products on the average farm makes impossible any accurate determination of money costs of production per unit of product.

Joint costs take other forms also. A farmer whose principal crop was wheat found that he could raise some corn with little increase in the cost of labor. His labor bill on 50 acres of wheat was $500 for the year. He could raise 30 acres of corn at a labor cost of $400. But he could raise 50 acres of wheat and 30 acres of corn with a labor bill of $600. To these two crops he might add 20 acres of hay and 10 milk cows, and increase his labor bill to only $650. In such a case it is impossible to divide the expenses for labor among enterprises, even though one can easily tell how many hours were spent on each crop. Therefore we find there is only one satisfactory method of determining which enterprises, and how much of each, to use in the farm business; that is, to employ as a basis the net income of the farm as a whole.

Complementary relationships between enterprises. Crop and livestock enterprises do not exist alone. Feeds must be raised for the livestock and, on the other hand, livestock must be kept to convert some low-grade crop materials, such as cornstalks, into marketable products. This is the *complementary relationship* between enterprises, which means that *some enterprises provide materials or services which are needed by others.* Corn and hog enterprises are complementary. The corn provides feed for the hogs, and the hogs are a more economical means of marketing the corn. Small grains are complementary to the hay crop, since they serve as nurse crops for the timothy or clover.

This complementary relationship is an important consideration in our selection of enterprises. We must always consider whether or not the enterprises we have included in our farm organization provide a means of utilizing everything that is produced, insofar as that is

profitable. Perhaps a livestock enterprise can be added
to make use of some crop product that has previously
been wasted, or a crop might be added to provide more
cheaply a feed which we have been buying.

Fig. 7.—Oat harvest supplements corn in the use of labor.

Supplementary relationship. We may add an enterprise *to utilize labor or equipment at times when there is
no demand for it by other enterprises.* This is known as
the *supplementary relationship.* To provide employment
for his labor during the winter, the farmer may keep dairy
cows. In the crop-growing season, oats can be grown in
addition to corn without adding much to the labor bill.
Oats alone may not be a profitable crop, but they may
serve to increase the net income of the farm as a whole.

Enterprises may also supplement one another in using
equipment or even land which is not needed at the time

for other crops. Sweet clover planted in the oat crop furnishes pasture after the oats are removed and provides a use for the land during the latter part of the season. The sweet clover thus *supplements* the oat crop by making use of the land when it would otherwise be idle. The oat crop serves as a nurse crop to the clover and thereby provides a *complementary* relationship between these two crops. Also, the sweet clover helps to maintain or increase soil fertility for the benefit of the corn crop which is to follow, and thus provides a *complementary* relationship between the sweet clover and the corn.

Multiple Selection of Enterprises

We can now summarize the principles which must be followed in order to select those enterprises which will bring the highest returns. Simply stated, they are:

1. From each group of competing enterprises, select that enterprise which promises the greatest net return for the farm as a whole.

2. Combine with the main enterprises whatever complementary enterprises are needed to provide outlets for crops or to furnish sources of materials or services needed either by livestock or crops.

3. Finally, in order that any labor or other resource which is not being fully used by these enterprises can be made to contribute to the income, select as a supplementary enterprise some enterprise which will utilize it.

The whole group of enterprises should yield the highest net return for the use of the farmer's resources, and no enterprise should be added if it seems likely to reduce the net income. Each enterprise should be increased in size as long, and only as long, as it promises to increase the net income.

References

Black, John D., and Black, A. G., *Production Organization*, Holt, New York, 1926, Chapter XI.

Gray, L. C., *Introduction to Agricultural Economics*, Macmillan, New York, 1924, Chapter IX.

Holmes, C. L., *Economics of Farm Organization and Management*, Heath, Boston, 1928, Chapter XIV.

Taylor, H. C., *Outlines of Agricultural Economics*, Macmillan, New York, 1925, Chapter IV.

Warren, G. F., *Farm Management*, Macmillan, New York, 1916, Chapter III.

CHAPTER IV

Obtaining the Use of a Farm

The Problem: In choosing a farm, what should a farmer look for? What are the steps to ownership? Is it always desirable to become an owner? Might it be preferable, under some conditions, to remain a renter?

Characteristics of a Desirable Farm

Acquiring the use of a farm is the first step in the career of every farmer. Although a few gain their farms through inheritance, most farmers are not so fortunate. There are two phases to the problem: (1) What sort of farm should one choose? (2) How can the use of such a farm be obtained?

A farm is both a place to make a living and a place to live. When selecting a farm, keep both these points in mind.

Fertility of land. The fertility of the land is one of the most important considerations. If a soil survey map is available, it should be consulted so that the soil types of the farm can be identified. Not all soils of the same type are equally productive. Moreover, the present condition of the soil should be studied. Has its fertility been depleted? If so, could it be built up again within a reasonable period of time and without too great expense?

When considering building up run-down soil, note the kind of improvement it needs. Is the soil too open and

49

sandy? Is it composed of clay or gumbo, which puddles easily and is hard to work in wet seasons? Does it need liming? Is it so deficient in organic matter that it will require liberal applications of barnyard or green manure? Last, and very important, what will it *cost* to restore the fertility of the soil? Remember that the cost of the farm includes necessary improvements or repairs as well as the original purchase price.

Topography or the lay of the land. Topography, the lay of the land, cannot be changed by the farmer. The land should have natural drainage or a drainage system capable of carrying off excess rainfall before it damages the crops. Some fields which raise good crops in normal seasons become ponds in wet years. However, there is much level land which can be drained and made highly productive. If a drainage system is necessary, its probable cost should be estimated before the farm is purchased.

At the other extreme is land which is too hilly and rough to be very productive. If the slope is too steep and the soil erodes easily, it will be necessary either to keep the rougher parts of the farm in permanent pasture or go to the trouble and expense of controlling erosion. Even with erosion control, yields on the steeper hillsides are apt to be unsatisfactory and the expense of farming rough land is high.

Slopes may need to be terraced, or contour farming followed. Terracing is expensive, and contour farming likewise increases the cost of operation. It is possible, of course, to purchase or rent rough land at a price which takes these handicaps into account, but the common tendency has been to overvalue rough and poor land.

Improvements. Even if the soil and topography are satisfactory, the farm still may not be a "good buy" if the improvements are inadequate or in poor condition. Buildings, fences, and a water supply system are as necessary as the land. If these are lacking or are in poor repair, how much would it cost to supply or repair them?

Buildings should be investigated carefully. Is their arrangement convenient? Is the house adequate and in good repair? The future comfort of the farmer and his family will depend largely upon the condition of the house. Incidentally, if one is going to rent a farm, the condition of the house will tell a good deal about the character of the prospective landlord.

Frequently landlords consider that money spent in improving the farm house brings little return. If the landlord is stingy or pressed for money, the house is likely to lack improvements or be in poor repair. Such a house does not speak well for the future relationships of tenant and landlord. On the other hand, a well-planned house in good repair and with modern conveniences indicates an enterprising and conscientious landlord with whom one should expect to have satisfactory relations. Both conclusions, of course, assume that the present landlord has held the farm for some time.

The condition and size of other buildings also tell much about the farm itself as well as its owner. If the corn cribs, granaries, haymows, and barns are small, they do not speak well for the productivity of the land. The buildings should be adapted to the type of farming for which the land is best suited. Beef-cattle equipment on a farm suited to dairying is obviously a serious handicap.

Farm layout. A farm may be highly productive and yet have its buildings and fields so inconveniently located as to prevent its efficient operation. How much will the desirable changes cost, and how long will it take to

make them?   Will the landlord agree to them if the farm
is to be rented?

Weeds and stumps.   Before taking a farm, see if there
are on the land any patches of troublesome weeds or any
stumps or rocks that need to be removed.   Some of the
more persistent weeds cost $30 or $40 per acre to eradi-
cate.   A patch of creeping jenny, quack grass, or canada
thistle may be a more serious handicap than if that much
land were not there at all.   Until the pest is eradicated,
it means trouble, expense, and unproductive labor—sometimes for several years.

Location of farm and roads.   For some types of farming, such as the production of fluid milk, it is necessary
that a market town or shipping point be easily accessible.
The distance from market and the kinds of roads are very
important.   The buying of supplies and the social life
of the family, as well as the marketing of farm produce,
are affected by these considerations.

Taxes.   Taxes represent a deduction from earnings of
the farm that go to pay for public services.   In some
localities interest on old public debts increases the taxes
without resulting in current benefits.   Districts with con-
solidated schools are likely to have higher taxes than those
with one-room schoolhouses.   Counties with a large mileage of improved roads will probably have correspondingly
higher road taxes.   Drainage taxes should also be investigated.   Remember, however, that taxes of this sort
represent payments for benefits received.   The important
question is not the amount of taxes but whether they are
high or low in proportion to the benefits received.

In some cases all taxes are paid by the landowner, in
others some taxes, such as road and school, are paid by
the tenant under the terms of the lease.   In the latter

cases the taxes should be considered in determining the amount of rent.

The community. The kind of community in which the farm is located is an important factor. The amount of satisfaction derived from living on a particular farm depends to a large extent upon the kind of neighborhood and the presence of good schools and churches. Are the neighbors congenial? Are they progressive, and do they work together well? These questions are important both from a social and a business standpoint. Many farm tasks can be best performed by working together and exchanging labor. Industrious neighbor boys are the most desirable hired labor. In other ways also, such as the cooperative marketing of farm products, the individual farmer depends to a large extent upon his neighbors.

Buying or Renting a Farm

In America the ambitious farm boy looks forward to owning his own farm. Is this always desirable? How can the ownership of a farm be achieved?

Advantages of farm ownership. The economic independence that comes with owning a farm is the first consideration that appeals to the beginning or tenant farmer. The owner-farmer can farm as he pleases, provided he is not heavily indebted and subject to control by his creditors. He can select his own cropping and livestock systems. He can arrange his fields and buildings for convenience and economy.

The owner-operator has the greatest incentive to progressive farming. Such factors as soil improvement yield returns only after a period of time. On his own farm the farmer can feel confident that he will reap the benefits from such improvements. On a rented farm the land-lord may be unwilling to invest in lime, drainage, or ter-racing, and, if the tenant makes such improvements at his own expense, he is not sure of staying on the farm long enough to get the benefits. If he does stay, his rent may be raised because the farm earns more with such improve-ments than without them.

A strong inducement to land ownership in the United States during the past has been the fact that the owner receives the benefit of any rise in land prices. From the end of the Civil War to the end of the World War the price of land in many sections of Iowa increased at a rate of over 6 percent compound interest. Under those condi-tions a landowner could make a good return from the growth of his investment without any current earnings. The most profitable policy for a young farmer was to get title to a farm as soon as possible.

Price trends are not always favorable to farm owner-ship, however. During the period from 1920 to 1932, prices of farm land fell rapidly and many farmers who had bought farms on what they thought was a safe margin lost their land. While it is profitable to own property during periods of rising prices, it is unprofitable and may be disastrous during periods of falling prices if the land is not paid for in full.

Advantages of renting land. When prices of land fall or stay at the same level, there are advantages to the young farmer in renting rather than owning land. He may not have sufficient capital to buy a farm. By renting he can have the use of a farm and obtain the returns from oper-ating it. If the landlord has been a successful farmer himself, the beginner may have the benefit of his advice and experience. Since this advantage may be obtained only under certain types of tenancy, it is important to choose wisely the proper type of lease as well as landlord and farm.

Another advantage in renting is that investment in farm equipment and livestock generally has a faster turnover and can yield a higher rate than investment in land or buildings. A man with limited capital can, therefore, get ahead faster financially if he invests his funds in current and working assets, instead of tying them up in land. Still another advantage is the flexibility in renting: a larger farm or one of a different type can be obtained much more readily if the farmer is not tied down by ownership.

The tenant may weather the storm more easily. How large a down payment should be made in buying a farm? The usual rule is one half or, in the interests of safety, never less than a third. With too small a payment, a poor crop year or a period of unfavorable prices may seriously embarrass the farmer. A heavily indebted owner, continually badgered by creditors, is a most unenviable person. A tenant, on the other hand, may have to "tighten his belt" for awhile, but he is more likely to weather the storm and have a less unpleasant time doing it.

To rent or to own? Suppose that a mortgage loan cost $4\frac{1}{2}$ percent, while the net earnings from investment in land amount to only 3 percent. In this case a farmer who has made a down payment of a third will be paying out the entire earnings on his land to meet his interest obligations. He will receive no earnings at all on his own investment. If he had rented a farm and invested his money elsewhere, he would have been better off, unless there is an increase in land values.

Before investing, consider carefully the relationship between the net earnings and the price of land. The net earnings consist of the gross rent received by the owner minus taxes, depreciation on improvements, expenses for upkeep or improvements, and similar items. A gross rent of $6 per acre may yield only $4 or $4.50 after these deductions have been made. If the net return is $4 and the interest rate on conservative, long-time investments is 5 per cent, the capitalization of the net returns would mean a price of $80 per acre. If the interest rate were expected to be 4 percent, the capitalization process (dividing the net earnings of $4 by the rate .04) would suggest a price of $100. In buying a farm, compare its net earning power with the purchase price to see what rate the investment will yield.

Non-economic influences on land prices. The price may be influenced by considerations other than purely business ones. There is a popular prejudice toward paying higher prices (or accepting lower returns) because land represents in some way a "safe" and "stable" investment. It is true that the land's physical characteristics (if carefully maintained) change but little, but the last few years have shown that the *value* of land may be anything but stable.

If a large number of potential land buyers believe that higher prices for farm products or farm land are probable in future years, they may be induced to pay higher prices than current earnings justify. This is called a *speculative value*.

There are likewise certain sentimental values which attach to land in some areas and in special cases. A man may be willing to pay too much for a farm on which he was raised or to which he has some sentimental attachment. In England, ownership of land carries with it some feeling of social superiority, and well-to-do families are willing to pay more for land than they would for other investments yielding the same return. Because of its high price, therefore, most English farmers do not own their land.

When the English farmer makes a profit, he is inclined to invest in something other than land. This would be a good practice for many farmers in the United States. By having investments in industries other than agriculture, the farmer avoids "putting all his eggs in one basket" and may thus secure greater financial safety as well as a more stable income.

The Agricultural Ladder

The term *agricultural ladder* refers to the steps by which a young farmer climbs to land ownership. The three most important steps are: hired man, tenant, and owner. One of these rungs, of course, may be skipped or replaced by another.

When land was relatively cheap in comparison to wages, it was not hard for a young man, by working as a farm hand, to save enough money in a short time to set himself up as a tenant farmer. With higher-priced land and the need for a greater investment in equipment and livestock, the achievement is more difficult, but it can still be done. There is also the advantage of learning from his employers while he is saving the necessary capital.

In many cases the farm boy works at home for wages for a few years and is helped financially by his family when he is ready to start farming for himself. Other boys continue working on their home farms and ultimately take over the management when their fathers are ready to retire. Some are so fortunate as to inherit their farms outright. Some inherit a share in a farm and buy the rest from the other heirs. As the country becomes more urbanized, an increasing number of farm boys find employment in businesses in towns while they accumulate enough money to start farming.

Fig. 8.—A well-kept rented farm.

Tenant farming is the second step toward farm ownership. In former days, when land was relatively cheap, this stage was often short. Higher land prices, particularly in proportion to annual earnings, have recently made this step a much longer one. In sections with the highest land prices the ordinary farmer can scarcely earn and save enough during his lifetime to become an owner. Where land is cheaper, it is still possible to attain ownership but naturally the property is less productive and less valuable.

The third step toward complete ownership usually is operation under mortgaged ownership. Many men acquire title to a farm by borrowing a large part of the purchase price on a mortgage, and then spend a number of years paying off the mortgage. Mortgaged ownership has some advantages over tenancy if prices of land and farm products do not decline. The mortgaged owner can usually operate the farm as he sees fit, and realizes the benefit from any improvements that he makes or any increase in land prices that may occur.

Characteristics of a Desirable Farm Tenancy System

A 200-acre farm, with land worth $125 per acre, represents an investment of $25,000. Not many young men are able to earn and save this amount. As land values rise, ownership becomes more difficult and tenancy more common. We hear much of the disadvantages and the social undesirability of tenancy. Does this mean that we are doomed to an agriculture which is unprogressive and destructive of natural resources?

Progressive agriculture *can* be followed under a system of tenancy. Only a very small percentage of the farms of England are operator-owned, and yet English agriculture is most progressive in certain respects. There has been excellent maintenance of soil and improvements. The tenancy system, however, does lend itself to abuse of the land where there is not a strong tradition of land conservation, in addition to favorable farm laws. Evidently there are desirable as well as undesirable systems of tenancy. What are the characteristics of a good system?

By the terms of the lease a landowner grants to a

tenant the right to use the land for farming purposes for a specified period of time and in return for a stated payment. Unfortunately the interests of landlord and tenant do not coincide in all respects and sometimes may be in direct opposition. Each party is likely to be interested in immediate returns and may neglect the maintenance of the farm in trying to secure the highest current income.

Conservation of the land. The land may be regarded as an interested third party to the agreement, and society is entitled to protect the interests of posterity in our natural resources. Much can be done in this direction by the development of public opinion which regards with disfavor farming practices that permit depletion of soil fertility or erosion of the land. In the meantime, conservation of fertility and control of erosion should be provided for in the leases.

Mutually profitable farming methods. The lease should permit the tenant to follow a type of farming which is well adapted to the neighborhood and which is advantageous to the tenant. He should not be prevented from following progressive practices so long as they do not result in injury to the farm.

Remuneration for improvements. Tenants should be encouraged to make improvements, apply fertilizer, lime, and so on. But they cannot be expected to go to this expense without some assurance that, when they leave the farm, they will be repaid for any unexhausted value. The landlord may feel he cannot afford to make the improvements the tenant desires, and the tenant of course cannot afford to make improvements from which he may not realize the benefit.

Explicit, written lease. The agreement between the tenant and the landlord should be in the form of a definite, written lease which states specifically what each party is to do. This will avoid misunderstanding later on.

Date of beginning and end of lease. The lease should state clearly when the contract begins and ends. It should also state the terms under which it may be terminated at any time, what notice is required by either party, and the terms under which it is to be continued in case no notice is given.

Payment of rent. In the case of cash rent, the exact amount that will be due and the method by which it is to be paid should be set forth clearly, as well as the dates when payments are to be made. Dates of payment should correspond as nearly as possible to dates of sale of important crops. With share renting, the lease should specify the landlord's share and also the methods by which measurements are to be made or records kept. Any necessary records should be accessible to the landlord at all times.

Provisions to be made by each party. The lease should state clearly what each party is to furnish. The farm should be described, its location and acreage given. Any other property, equipment, or livestock to be furnished by the landlord should be stated as specifically as possible. The lease should also specify what equipment, livestock, power, labor, and so on, are to be provided by the tenant.

Limitations on the tenant. It may be desirable to place certain limitations on the tenant. If so, they should be set forth definitely in the lease. For example, on a crop share farm the tenant might feed from undivided crops enough hogs or poultry for family use. In such a case the maximum number of animals should be mentioned. In other cases it may be provided that these be fed from the tenant's share of crops.

Removal of roughage from the farm. The landlord will, as a means of preventing depletion of fertility, usually wish to prohibit the removal of straw, hay, or fodder from the farm. A specific clause to that effect should be inserted in the lease.

Division of joint expenses. On a share rented farm there are generally some expenses, such as threshing bills, twine, and so on, that are shared by tenant and landlord. The proportions and manner in which joint expenses are to be shared should be stated clearly to avoid uncertainty and disagreement.

Division of income. For share rented farms the problem of sharing the various elements of income should be covered in the lease. The proportion in which each type of income is to be divided and the method of keeping sales records should be stated. If some items, such as dairy products, are to be sold through a definite channel, the lease might provide that the creamery mail separate checks to tenant and landlord.

The division of the various products should bear some relation to the respective contributions of tenant and landlord. The tenant frequently receives a larger proportion of such things as potatoes and truck crops, which require a larger amount of labor than corn or wheat.

Protection of interests of parties concerned. Leases frequently contain provisions for guarantees of tenant and landlord. It is not uncommon to provide for a chattel mortgage on the tenant's property, or some similar arrangement, in case of non-payment of rent.

Division of joint property. If there is jointly owned property, as under a livestock share lease, it is necessary to provide for a definite method of division when the lease ends.

Arbitration. It is well to provide in the lease for arbitration in case of disagreement. The usual method is for tenant and landlord each to name one arbitrator and these two then select a third. The three so named investigate the disagreement and make a decision, which is to be considered final.

Common Forms of Tenancy

Cash renting. Renting for a definite amount of cash is probably the simplest form of tenancy and is ordinarily the most advantageous to the experienced tenant. Both landlord and tenant are sure of the amount to be paid.

The landlord usually furnishes only land and buildings. He is obliged to maintain the improvements on the farm and pays the taxes. It is sometimes stipulated that the tenant make minor repairs on fences and buildings but that the landlord furnish all repair materials. To the landlord the cash lease has the advantage of requiring less supervision of the farm and less risk in the amount of returns. There is apt to be less friction between landlord and tenant since the amount of rent is definitely stated.

To the tenant the advantages of the cash lease are: He can plan his own farming system with little interference. He receives, above the amount of the rent, full benefit from his own good management. Cash rent is usually somewhat lower than share rent would be on the same farm, because the landlord does not have to share the risk or supervise the farm.

Crop share renting. Under the crop share lease the landlord also furnishes land, buildings, and improvements and keeps all property and equipment in repair. The tenant furnishes all labor, equipment, and horses. Expenses for seed, fertilizer, threshing, and twine are sometimes divided between landlord and tenant. The horses may be fed from the tenant's share or from the undivided crops. In the latter case the landlord usually shares the fuel bill for the tractor.

Fig. 9.—A run-down, crop share farm.

A certain share of the crops, $\frac{1}{2}$, $\frac{2}{5}$, $\frac{1}{3}$, is the landlord's rent. Usually the tenant is required to haul the landlord's share to market or a shipping point. The tenant may keep whatever livestock he chooses if they are fed from his own share of crops. Pasture and hay land is usually rented for a definite cash rent, even on crop share farms. The landlord exerts some supervision over the farm and runs some risk as to the tenant's honesty.

The tenant has an advantage in running less risk from a small crop or low prices. He can also expect from the landlord more assistance in management than if he paid cash rent. The yearly average of rent will be somewhat higher, however, in return for these advantages.

The crop share system has the serious disadvantage of being hard on the farm. Since the landlord's share of produce is sold each year and the tenant may, as he is entitled to do, sell a large part of his, the fertility of the land is apt to be seriously depleted.

Stock share renting. This system is commonly found in dairy areas or in other sections where livestock are an essential part of the farm. With this form of lease the landlord also furnishes the land and improvements, plus half the livestock (except workstock) and half the feed, seed, and so on. The tenant furnishes labor, equipment (together with its upkeep), and workstock, in addition to his half of the livestock and feed. Other operating expenses are usually divided equally.

Under this system all receipts from the farm are shared equally. They represent returns from a large amount of capital (partly provided by the landlord) and from the land, and also reflect the results of the landlord's supervision. Landlord and tenant must work together and agree about rotations, number of livestock, and methods of feeding and caring for them. This plan is ideal for the young farmer who needs experience but lacks capital, and for the landlord who lives near his farm and has time and interest for its supervision. Usually the landlord's returns are higher than if he rented for cash or crop share, and he has the added assurance that his land will be well taken care of.

These different methods of renting have, of course, many variations. Incomes from certain crops may be shared, or expenses divided, in other ways. Only typical cases have been discussed here.

Share-cropping. In the southern part of the United States there is a system of tenure under which the landlord furnishes more and has closer control over the farm operations than in any of the systems described in the preceding paragraphs. Under the share-cropping system the landlord furnishes land, buildings, equipment, and workstock. He may even loan the cropper funds to buy groceries. In return for a share, usually half, plus house rent and garden, the cropper furnishes the labor to raise and harvest the crop.

The cropper differs little from a hired man, except that he receives for his work half the crop instead of a fixed wage. The plans are made by the landlord or plantation owner, who also directs how they are to be carried out each day. This system is often used when crops require a large amount of labor and when the tenant has little or no capital of his own.

References

Gray, L. C., *Introduction to Agricultural Economics*, Macmillan, New York, 1924, Chapter XV.

Taylor, H. C., *Outlines of Agricultural Economics*, 1925, Chapters XXI-XXV, Macmillan, New York, 1925.

Indiana Extension Bulletin 134: "Giving the Tenant a Chance," by Lynn Robertson, 1925.

Iowa Bulletin 214: "Relation of Types of Tenancy to Types of Farming in Iowa," by C. L. Holmes, 1923.

Iowa Circular 87: "Drawing Up the Farm Lease," by C. L. Holmes, 1923.

Kansas Circular 155: "The Stock Share Lease," by W. E. Grimes, 1930.

Maryland Bulletin 352: "Farm Tenancy and Leasing Systems in Maryland," by W. P. Walker and S. H. DeVault, 1933.

Michigan Circular Bulletin 102: "Farm Leasing Systems in Michigan," by F. T. Riddell, 1927.

Minnesota Special Bulletin 153: "Suggestions on Farm Leases," by William L. Cavert, 1932.

Nebraska Bulletin 210: "Steps to Nebraska Farm Ownership," by J. O. Rankin, 1926.

Ohio Bulletin 348: "Methods of Renting Land in Ohio," by J. I. Falconer, 1921.

Pennsylvania Bulletin 232: "Farm Tenancy and Lease Forms in Pennsylvania," by J. E. McCord, 1929.

Tennessee Circular 20: "What Should Be in the Rental Contract," by C. E. Allred, 1929.

U. S. Department of Agriculture, Farmers Bulletin 1088: "Selecting a Farm," by E. H. Thomas, 1935.

Part II

ORGANIZING THE FARM: BASIC PRINCIPLES

CHAPTER V

Organizing the Farm and the Farmer's Resources

The Problem: How can the farm be organized to produce the greatest returns? As a first step, how shall the farmer go about taking an inventory to find out what his resources are?

Effective Farm Management

A farmer who owns his farm decides that it is not so profitable as it should be. He has not made any systematic effort to reorganize it or to discard unprofitable enterprises, but wants to know how to proceed toward effective management.

He must study the entire farm business, considering each crop and whether or not it could be replaced by a more profitable one. He should see if the livestock enterprises are yielding satisfactory returns for feed, labor, and shelter. Are the expenditures for labor and equipment too high? Above all, are the farm enterprises working smoothly together. Even if a project seems to be doing well, he must question whether it is adding to the net income of the farm as a whole, and if it is as profitable as some other enterprise that might be substituted for it.

The Factors of Production

A farm budget or plan is a complicated affair. Of just what does a farm consist? Perhaps we had better start

by making a survey of the farm to find out exactly what
are the resources with which we have to work. We shall
find *four basic factors of production:*

1. Land.
2. Labor.
3. Capital.
4. Management.

1. Land. Our first resource is land. Every type of
business, store, factory, or railroad needs the use of some
land, but in farming that factor plays a particularly
significant part. As far as its market value is concerned,
land is usually the most important of the farm resources.

Just what is land? The farmer usually thinks of his
land as the area on which he grows his crops or pastures
his livestock. To him the essential element is the soil,
and its *fertility* is his most important consideration.
However, there is much more to be considered. The land
may be level or rough, and its *topography* is a feature the
farmer cannot change. The *location* of each piece
of land is closely related to its usefulness. *Climate* is
closely related to location and is of great importance in
crop raising. Location also involves advantages or disadvantages in regard to *distance to market.* All of these
matters affect the usefulness of agricultural land, and if
any one of them is decidedly unfavorable the farm may
have little or no value as a producing unit.

Land includes much more than the surface used in
agriculture. There is forest land and mineral-bearing
areas whose surface may or may not be of agricultural
use. There are areas used for industrial and transportation purposes, as well as for amusement. In a broad sense,
land includes all the natural factors of production.

The usefulness of natural factors of production varies greatly. Mineral beds differ in richness and in the ease with which they may be worked. Some city lots are worth more than others. The same amount of labor and capital used in operating a store on a busy corner may yield many times as much as a similar store in the suburbs. Farm land likewise differs in productivity. A fertile and level field may yield twice as much for the same amount of work and fertilizer as a sandy or a hilly field nearby. For this reason a farmer can afford to pay much more for the first field than for the second.

2. **Labor.** This factor cannot be evaluated for the purposes of an inventory, but labor is an essential factor of production. A farmer's supply of labor, the amount of work that he and his family can do during the year, is one of the most important things to consider in planning the farm program.

Labor is the active element of production. The forces of nature in and of themselves are seldom of immediate use. In economic production *labor is used to make things more useful by changing their form, their location, or their time of consumption.*

Labor is used to control natural forces in such a way as to produce a crop of wheat from the plant food elements in the soil, the radiation of the sun, and the oxygen and carbon dioxide in the air. The usefulness of products may be increased by changing their location—for example, by moving wheat from the areas where it is produced to the cities where it is to be consumed. There its usefulness is further increased by changing it into bread. The usefulness of part of a crop may be increased by changing the time when it is to be used. A bushel of fruit becomes, by having been stored until winter, more useful than it would have been at the height of the fruit season.

In each case the labor must be partly with the hands and partly with the mind. The planning of a warehouse is just as important to the storage of apples as is the labor of moving the fruit in or out of the building. Production should not be considered solely as the extraction of physical goods from the land.

Fig. 10.—Large amounts of capital are used in such enterprises as cattle feeding.

Labor used by the farmer in the operation of his farm may be classified as: (1) the operator's own labor, (2) that of his family, and (3) hired labor. In order to obtain the greatest returns, the farmer must plan to have work to do himself during as much of the year as possible. Help should be hired when there is work to be done which will add more to the farm income than the amount of the wages the farmer will have to pay. If labor must be hired, it is better to plan to use it continuously. The farm will run more smoothly, the help will be more competent, and there will not be any loss of time from looking for occasional help.

3. Capital. A third factor of production consists of capital goods. These are man-made goods, such as machines, fertilizers, feeds, livestock, buildings, fences, and so on, which are being used in further production.

In farm records or other accounts the term *capital* may be used to mean the net investment in a business, regardless of the form in which it is invested. On a balance sheet, land may appear as one of the elements in which "capital" has been invested, although land has not been created by man and has some important differences from man-made capital goods. Mortgages, bonds, or notes owed to the proprietor are also counted among the resources on the balance sheet, although these do not represent basic factors of production and are simply claims against the property of some other person or firm.

The capital goods on a farm may be conveniently classified according to the length of their normal productive life. Four general groups are:

(1) Fixed capital or equipment.
(2) Moveable equipment.
(3) Livestock.
(4) Materials, or circulating capital.

(1) *Fixed capital or equipment.* By this term is meant those man-made goods which are normally used for a considerable time before they are worn out or their usefulness is exhausted. Fixed capital includes buildings which, if properly cared for, may last from 10 to 100 years or more. Fences and drainage or water systems which may be used 20 or 30 years also come under this group.

(2) *Moveable equipment.* This means farm machinery, tractors, trucks, brooders, incubators, moveable hog houses, and the like. Tools and implements which are normally used more than one season are also included. The purpose of moveable equipment is to permit labor to be employed more effectively. This is equally true for the smallest hand tool and for the largest, most complicated machinery.

(3) *Livestock.* This term includes all breeding stock, workstock, and animals raised for their meat, milk, wool, or eggs. These three types serve quite different purposes. The workstock provides power. The breeding stock is kept for the production of other animals. The third group is either to be consumed directly as meat, or kept for the production of such consumable goods as milk, eggs, or wool.

(4) *Materials or circulating capital.* This includes things which are to be used for further production but are consumed in a single usage. Examples are feed for livestock, fuel used in generating steam in a boiler, seeds, fertilizer, and so on. Perhaps the fertilizer is not entirely used up by the first crop raised, but at any rate it cannot be gathered up and used over again.

Materials represent simply a stage in the production process. Feed crops may be raised as a step in the production of meat or milk. Coal may be mined as a step in the transportation of freight or passengers. Fertilizer may be used as an early stage in the production of crops.

4. Management. Management is the fourth factor of production. Its function is to plan what and how much to produce and how to produce it. The manager of a business organizes it—decides what factors of production he will need, how much of each is necessary, and what form each will take. In other words, he determines whether to use much equipment and a small amount of labor, or vice versa. He decides on the kind of equipment. Then he must operate the business and make daily decisions about the work to be done and the method of doing it. He must decide what to buy, and when and how to market his products. He agrees on the wages to be paid for hired help, on the rate of interest on borrowed capital, and on the rent to be paid the landlord. He must assume most of the risks of production. If he is successful he benefits from his good management, and his proper remuneration is known as the *profits* of business.

Taking the Inventory

These four fundamental resources—land, labor, capital, and management—the farmer must use in producing his crops and livestock and, indirectly, in producing his income. However, in taking an inventory, we find that it is impossible to put a dollars-and-cents value on two of these factors, labor and management, because they do not exist physically as things which may be transferred from person to person. This leaves only the land and the capital goods to be entered in our inventory.

An inventory is a list of assets on the one hand and liabilities, which are claims or debts against the business, on the other. An asset is something of value which either belongs to the owner of the business or is owed to him by someone else. The liabilities, on the other side of the balance sheet, are bills, notes, or mortgages which the owner owes to others.

A balance sheet or inventory summary is sometimes drawn up with the assets, or resources, on one side and the liabilities on the other, as shown below. Notice that the *Net Worth* of the business, that is, the amount by which the assets exceed the liabilities, causes the two lists to balance. The Net Worth is the value of the business over and above the claims of anyone outside the business.

In another common form of summary, the liabilities are placed on the same side with, but below, the list of

FARM BALANCE SHEET OR INVENTORY STATEMENT

Assets		Liabilities	
Land...................	$20,000	Mortgage...............	$12,000
Equipment..............	1,500	Notes Owed.............	2,500
Livestock..............	2,000	Bills Owed.............	1,000
Crops and Feeds........	4,000		
Bills and Notes Receivable	500	Net Worth.............	13,000
Cash..................	500		
	$28,500		$28,500

assets. This is called the *Comparative Inventory*. The form makes it easy to follow changes of individual items from year to year.

Table V is drawn up in this general comparative form; however, only the asset items are given here.

Two Steps in Taking Inventory

To take an inventory it is first necessary to make an actual, physical count. We must go over the farm and count the various kinds of livestock and approximate their weight if they are to be sold for meat. The amount of crops or feed on hand must be estimated as closely as possible, and the pieces of machinery listed and their condition noted. All this should be done on the same day if possible.

The second step is to place valuations on the assets listed. Conservative valuations should be used. The market price is the usual basis, but it should be adjusted to the value of the product at the farm. In case of a product which the farmer usually sells, he should subtract the estimated cost of getting it to market. If it is one that he ordinarily buys, he should add the cost of getting it to the farm.

The only practical method of evaluating the land is to use a conservative estimate of the price for which it could be sold. Current prices for similar land in the neighborhood may be a guide.

These inventory valuations should be made carefully in order to show the actual worth of the business. In case of doubt, too low a valuation is better than one that is too high, because the latter may encourage the farmer to go too far in debt.

Classification of Assets

In drawing up an inventory, we group together those assets which have similar functions in the farm business. They will be grouped according to the enterprises of which they are a part, or according to their purpose in relation to other enterprises. Their ordinary classification as *fixed, working,* and *current* assets is based largely on their length of life. Within each of these main divisions they are further classified according to their functions or to the enterprises in which they are used. Table V shows a classification of the assets on five groups of Iowa farms.

Fixed assets. Fixed assets are those resources which last for a long time. Because of its permanence, land is perhaps the best example of this type of asset. Long-lived improvements, such as buildings, fences, and tile

TABLE V

COMPARISON OF AVERAGE INVENTORIES
ON GROUPS OF FARMS

Type of Farm	Hog	Beef Feeders	Beef Raisers	Dairy	General
Average No. of Acres.........	281	328	331	199	200
No. of Farms................	9	19	14	21	24
Current Assets:					
Cattle (fat & young).......	$ 551	$ 3,304	$ 1,316	$ 338	$ 429
Hogs.....................	834	590	557	235	283
Poultry..................	107	69	136	115	82
Sheep....................	62	58	51	18	205
Feeds....................	1,193	2,003	1,262	732	839
Seeds & Supplies...........	187	146	281	92	98
Total Current Assets.....	$ 2,934	$ 6,170	$ 3,603	$ 1,530	$ 1,936
Working Assets:					
Cattle—Breeding Stock.....	$ 451	$ 310	$ 1,740	$ 856	$ 518
Horses...................	488	524	594	339	404
Tractor..................	392	411	290	197	118
Equipment...............	1,284	1,677	1,298	891	822
Truck & Auto (farm share)..	98	288	212	162	141
Total Working Assets.....	$ 2,713	$ 3,210	$ 4,135	$ 2,445	$ 2,003
Total Current & Working Assets..................	$ 5,647	$ 9,380	$ 7,738	$ 3,976	$ 3,939
Fixed Assets					
Buildings & Improvements..	$ 8,692	$ 8,646	$ 5,952	$ 4,584	$ 4,356
Land.....................	19,480	23,134	24,535	11,593	15,595
Total Fixed Assets.......	$28,172	$31,779	$30,486	$16,177	$19,950
Total Business Assets........	$33,819	$41,159	$38,223	$20,152	$23,890
Value of Dwelling............	$ 4,094	$ 3,756	$ 3,246	$ 1,985	$ 2,263
Total Capital Managed.......	$37,913	$44,915	$41,469	$22,137	$26,153

drains, are also listed in this group. Two fundamentally different types of assets have been included here: land, which is a gift of nature; and long-lived capital goods, such as buildings.

Working assets. Working assets are resources which ordinarily will be used more than one year but which can be moved, as contrasted with buildings or fences. These include sources of power, horses, tractors, trucks, and the farm share of the automobile. Breeding stock and also producing stock, such as dairy cows that are not intended to be sold before the close of the current year, are also included. This group represents the farmer's equipment for producing marketable goods.

Current assets. Current assets are those products which are intended to be sold within the current year. They include crops, fattening steers, hogs, and poultry. Farmers often list their entire herd of hogs, because they cannot tell at inventory time which sows they will keep over into the following year.

The percentage of total capital that is invested in current assets is a commonly accepted test of the flexibility of a business. When it is small, the farmer is likely to have difficulty if a need for considerable ready cash arises.

The percentage of capital invested in both current and working assets compared to the investment in land and other fixed assets indicates whether or not the business is sufficiently flexible over a period of years. Farms are often overequipped or overstocked. We frequently find tractors or combines on farms that do not really need them, or too much livestock for the size of the farm.

Classification of liabilities. Liabilities are also classified on the basis of the length of the period they are to run. Mortgages and other long-time obligations are usually entered as separate items to distinguish them from short-time notes and bills which are due. The dates when such obligations are due should be kept well in mind and plans made for their payment or refinancing.

Net worth. The net worth is the amount by which the value of the assets exceeds that of the liabilities. *The net worth indicates the value of the proprietor's interest in the business.* It shows how much he would have left if he were to sell the farm and all that is on it and pay off all bills or other debts. When the liabilities are greater than the assets, the net worth becomes a negative figure and the business is said to be *insolvent* or *bankrupt*.

The changes in net worth from year to year indicate the growth or progress of the business. Most farmers want either to enlarge their businesses or to strengthen their financial standing. However, the farm profit or net income for the year does not necessarily mean a corresponding increase in net worth. A farmer may have a profit of $2,000 for the year but may spend it all for a new car and a trip for the family, and consequently his net worth is no larger than the year before. Or, he may live very economically and be able to pay off $1,000 worth of bills. Or, he may use that amount in buying livestock or equipment. In both of these cases his net worth is $1,000 greater at the end of the year.

References

Black, John D., *Production Economics*, Holt, New York, 1926, Chapters XIV-XVII.

Holmes, C. L., *Economics of Farm Organization and Management*, Heath, Boston, 1928, Chapters VII-X.

Hopkins, John A., *Farm Records*, Collegiate Press, Ames, Iowa, 1936, Chapters IV-V.

Taylor, H. C., *Outlines of Agricultural Economics*, Macmillan, New York, 1924, Chapters VIII-X.

CHAPTER VI

Budgeting and Planning

The Problem: What are the characteristics of a good farm plan or budget? What principles must the farmer keep in mind in planning his farm organization?

The Farm Budget

After the farmer has taken an inventory of his resources, his next problem is to plan a profitable organization. If his farm is already in operation, he will want to find out if he can improve his crop and livestock systems. How should he go about formulating his plan?

Does the practical farmer follow a budget? The practical method of checking over the farm plans and perhaps developing new ones is known as *farm budgeting.* In its complete form a farm budget includes a definite, written plan for the organization of the farm. In the following chapters we shall study the budget as a plan of farm organization.

Is it necessary to make out a formal, written plan? Although many practical farmers may not have a written plan, this need not mean that they have no plan. On the contrary, a farmer may have an excellent plan, despite the fact that he has never written down any part of it.

How do farmers develop their cropping systems in a particular neighborhood? How do they select their livestock enterprises and decide which machines to use in different operations? In general they depend on the accumulated experience of the neighborhood, as experiences and ideas are exchanged in conversation. Ideas and practices change slowly because most farmers are rather conservative about accepting new methods or crops until after they have seen them tried out by some of their more venturesome neighbors.

Fig. 11.—Farmers may change their plans because of price information obtained at outlook meetings.

This conservatism is in some ways a desirable thing, since it makes farming methods more stable. Many of the new ideas tried out will prove unsuccessful in that particular community, and the tendency of the farmer to "wait and see" keeps the majority from rushing first into one experiment and then into another. The common agricultural methods in any community are likely, for this reason, to be somewhat behind the most advanced practices, but they are nearly always being slowly improved. Information about new methods that have been developed is generally distributed by means of bulletins, farm papers, county agents, and agriculture teachers.

Where Does the Young Farmer Gain His Knowledge?

The young farmer has usually had experience on his father's farm and has observed the types of farm organization in the neighborhood. The experience of the community thus serves as a foundation for his own plan. He then tries to work out a fairly definite plan for the most productive crop system and the best way of disposing of his crops, either by direct sale or by livestock feeding. After his first year of experience as an actual farmer, he will probably revise some parts of the plan which did not work out as he had expected, but the rest of it he will repeat practically as it was.

However, old plans soon grow out of date and too much conservatism may make farmers too slow in mending their ways. Better methods may have been developed. Prices change, and what was a profitable crop may have become a very unprofitable one. A good example of this is the oat crop since the widespread adoption of tractors. Many farmers continue, merely from force of habit, to raise their same acreages of oats.

Certainly most of the successful farmers have a definite plan or budget. Those who farm from day to day, without plan, would profit by taking time to figure out what they are really doing. The outline of the budget given in the following chapters may seem elaborate and formal. In fact, describing how to make a budget is somewhat like telling a person how to use the correct silver at table. The practice is awkward and difficult to explain, but once it is understood and fixed in mind it becomes largely a matter of habit. Consequently we need first to go over the whole process carefully, in order not to miss any essential steps.

Scope of the Budget

The word *budget* means, to most of us, a plan for one's expenditures. But a plan for farm operation cannot be made up entirely in terms of prices and values. The budget must include all divisions of the farm. A farmer does not start out with the intention of raising $500 worth of hogs, or of buying $50 worth of tankage for them.

Physical data important. The physical resources which make up the farm determine the amount of a crop that can be raised. The amount of corn a farmer can raise will depend on the acreage available for it in a good rotation, as well as on the supply of labor during the growing season. In the budget this amount will be expressed in bushels rather than in dollars.

Similarly, the amount of a particular feed to be purchased will depend on the number of hogs to be raised, the weights at which they are to be marketed, and the quantity of home-grown supplements. Questions concerning values will be considered when we compare the relative prices of hogs and various feeds. If both corn and hogs are cheap, it may prove profitable to feed only small amounts of high-priced tankage. At any rate, when making out the budget we shall start with the amount of feed.

The budget will be simpler if we do not try to put a dollars-and-cents value on the items in it unless they represent purchases or sales made. This does not mean that financial results are unimportant. On the contrary, a satisfactory financial outcome is the main purpose of making the budget. However, the farm operation must be carried on in physical terms and only the results are measured in terms of money. Of course, any farm operation which involves actual buying or selling has a financial aspect, but there are in farm operation many steps in which there is no buying or selling.

Divisions of the Farm Budget

Crop system. In working out the farm budget, we find the crop system a good place to start because it determines the amount of feed crops available for livestock. The amount of labor, as well as power needed, also depends on the requirements of the crops during their growing and harvest seasons.

Soil fertility is one of the most important factors to consider in making out a crop plan. Our idea is not to raise crops that will bring in the most cash for this year, but to plan for the greatest returns over a long period of years. There must be a satisfactory rotation which will conserve fertility and prevent erosion. A successful rotation helps to control weeds and other pests; also, it must be planned to produce a group of crops that can be sold or used together in feeding livestock.

Livestock system. The next question is what to do with the crops after they are raised. What livestock enterprises will be able to use up the feed crops produced? The farmer must not plan for more livestock than he can handle with the available labor and equipment. These enterprises must give the maximum returns when labor required, equipment used, and feed consumed have each been considered.

The livestock section of the budget should not be planned to use up all crops as feed. Generally one or more cash crops must be included as a means of raising funds directly. The question of feeding or selling any crop depends, of course, on which procedure promises to be the more profitable. We should not consider livestock solely as a means of disposing of crops, nor should we plan for crops to be raised entirely for the benefit of the livestock.

Labor and power plans. In addition to plans for the crop and livestock systems, the farm budget should provide for the labor and power needed to carry out these enterprises satisfactorily. How much labor will they require during the busy season? Will they provide enough work to keep the available labor busy throughout the year? Sometimes additional enterprises, such as a small dairy, are included in the farm plans in order to give the farmer employment during the slack season.

How efficiently labor is used depends largely on the amount of power it employs and on the efficiency of the equipment through which the power is applied. A choice must be made between using horses exclusively, or a tractor, or a combination of both, as a source of farm power. We must also decide upon the number of horses or the size of the tractor needed. To do this we must first know how much power will be needed during the busiest seasons. Will there be available for horses feed which otherwise might have been wasted or used to poor advantage without them? If the feed can be sold or used for another purpose, we can compare the possible return from sale (plus the amount of labor the horses will require) with the cost of fuel and other expenses on the tractor.

Ordinarily we find on the medium-sized farm that horse power is more economical for certain farm operations and that the tractor is profitable only as supplementary power for the extra load during the busy season. This question of horses versus tractor will be discussed in more detail later.

The principal parts of the farm organization are then: the crop plan, the livestock plan, and the power and labor plan. The crop plan must provide for a satisfactory rotation in order to conserve soil fertility. The livestock enterprises are intended to use crops which cannot be sold to better advantage and to furnish full employment the year round. The power and labor plan insures that these enterprises will receive proper care at the right time. In making out this plan, the farmer will need to consider both the needs of the productive enterprises upon which he has decided and the full utilization of his own time.

Choice of alternative plans. How can the farmer choose between two enterprises both of which will adequately serve the same purpose in the farm business? He already knows the general principles that he should follow in organizing his farm. But where can he secure specific information? How can he know where to limit the size of each enterprise? Shall he feed one carload of steers and breed 20 sows, or feed two carloads of steers and breed only 10 sows? If soil fertility is not yet a serious problem on his farm and corn is his most profitable crop, how shall he know when to stop raising corn? Should he have one year of corn in a three-year rotation, two years in a five-year rotation, or two years in a four-year rotation?

The simplest way of choosing between two enterprises —or deciding how large an enterprise should be—is to make out two alternative budgets, in order to see which one promises to bring the larger net return. This is not a waste of work and in the long run will likely prove the more satisfactory procedure.

If we try to make such decisions by comparing cost and price, we soon find that costs vary with the size of the project and the makeup of the farm. The two enterprises cannot be considered independent of the rest of the farm, because products from a crop may serve as raw materials for a livestock project or for another crop. Trying out plans on paper may sometimes save the farmer the cost of expensive experiments, or show him the way to a larger net income.

Opportunity cost. The selection of enterprises often depends more upon losses or gains from other enterprises than upon the ones directly concerned. Deciding to raise more sheep may force the farmer to give up using a particular grain or roughage for dairy cows. Sheep also require a certain amount of labor that could be used for something else.

This consideration involves what is known as *opportunity cost*. When we decide to follow any specific plan, we must give up all the other plans that we might have followed. We must frequently make such choices in business planning. Hence we try to decide upon the plan that promises the greatest return from our resources. If we decide to feed more corn to hogs, that means, unless we buy corn, there will be just that much less for other livestock. If barley is planted in a certain field, it cannot be used that year to produce another crop.   In each case, selection of one enterprise means that we must forego the alternative opportunities.

The Most Profitable Combination of Enterprises

For his main enterprises the farmer selects, from the principal *competing* enterprises, those that promise to add most to his net income.   Then he selects *complementary* projects to provide raw materials for these, or to permit waste products from them to be utilized.   If there are farm resources not fully utilized by the two groups of enterprises, such as labor in slack seasons, the farmer will try to find other, or *supplementary*, enterprises to use up these possible wastes.

A flock of sheep may be a supplementary project. Sheep can make profitable use of low-grade roughage about the farm and require but little special equipment. Their care does not require much of the farmer's time, except at lambing time which occurs before his spring work begins.   As the size of the flock is increased, up to a certain point the income from the sheep grows more rapidly than the expense or trouble of keeping them. Twenty ewes can be cared for with little more trouble than ten, and thirty do not require half again as much labor as twenty.

As long as the unsalable roughage holds out, the profit from the flock increases.   If the flock increases beyond this point, however, it is necessary to feed the sheep higher-grade roughage, which might yield a greater return if fed to dairy cows or other livestock.   The flock will also have to be fed grain which could possibly be marketed to better advantage or fed to hogs or other stock.   Thus, increasing economy in one direction may be counteracted by a lowering of economy in another.

This illustration is typical of the practice of combining enterprises. The small dairy often pays better than the large one. The hog enterprise can pass the point of greatest profit, and this is true even in the heavy corn-producing regions of the Mid-West. If too many sows are bred, the farmer cannot take good care of them at farrowing time and consequently loses more pigs. The proportion of feeds that have to be purchased may increase. This means more than a proportionate increase in expense. With crops, a larger acreage of one means smaller acreages for the others. If the most profitable crop, such as corn, is put into the rotation too often, the yield soon declines. Moreover, as the farmer increases his acreage of this crop, he must also hire more labor for corn plowing and corn picking.

There is a most profitable size for each enterprise, as well as a most profitable enterprise for each purpose. As the size of an enterprise is increased on a certain farm, the net income from that farm increases up to a certain point. After this point any further increase in size of the project results in a smaller rather than a greater net return. This principle may be stated as follows:

On a given farm there is one most profitable combination of enterprises. Any change in this combination, either by increasing or decreasing the proportionate size of any enterprise, will result in a decrease in net returns.

How can we determine the best proportionate combination? After we have selected the various possible enterprises, we can locate the combination fairly well by changing their relative sizes until we are satisfied that no variation would increase the returns.   It is not necessary to make up completely new budgets for every possible variation in choice or size of the projects.   Alternative sections can be worked out for the parts of the business that would be affected.

References

Black, John D., *Production Economics*, Holt, New York, 1926, Chapter VIII.

Holmes, C. L., *Economics of Farm Organization and Management*, Heath, Boston, 1928, Chapter XIV.

Taylor, H. C., *Outlines of Agricultural Economics*, Macmillan, New York, 1924, Chapter IV.

CHAPTER VII

The Principle of Diminishing Physical Output

The Problem: At what point in the production of crops should the farmer stop applying fertilizer, seed, or labor? Does the crop yield vary directly with the amount of fertilizer or labor used? Does livestock production vary directly with the amount of feed, labor, or shelter?

"It Wouldn't Pay"

Two farmers are discussing the proper amount of fertilizer to use on the potato crop. Although they are agreed on the kind of fertilizer, one thinks that 500 pounds per acre is enough, whereas the other insists that a greater amount, perhaps 1,000 pounds, would increase the yield still further. The first man replies that, even if the second 500 pounds did increase the yield "it wouldn't pay."

Yield variation due to amount of fertilizer, labor, or other factors. Which of these two men is right? Would 1,000 pounds of fertilizer give a *greater* yield per acre than 500 pounds? Would the use of 1,000 pounds result in *twice* as many bushels as 500 pounds? Finally, would it *pay?* The last is the important question to the farmer. Before we can answer it, we must know what the difference in physical yields would be. Then we can come back to the question of economic returns.

Any farmer knows that a small amount of fertilizer may considerably increase his crop yield.   If he applies still more fertilizer, the yield may increase further.   But the second increase will, in all probability, be smaller than the one he obtained from the first application.   If he con-

Courtesy J. I. Case Co.

Fig. 12.—Potato production requires an intensive use of labor.

tinues to apply fertilizer, the responses will be smaller and smaller from each succeeding application.

Other elements in crop production besides fertilizer may also be varied in amount with corresponding changes in yield.   We may increase the amount of seed planted per acre or give our crop additional cultivation, and thus obtain a higher yield.   However, the increase in yield becomes proportionately smaller after a certain amount of seed or fertilizer or cultivation has been applied.

The Principle of Diminishing Physical Output

The tendency or law which we have just been discussing is known as the principle of *diminishing physical output.* It may be stated somewhat as follows:

When one of a group of production elements is increased in proportion to the others: (a) The output per added unit of the

Photo Schlecten Studio

Fig. 13.—A cattle ranch permits the extensive use of labor on low grade land.

variable factor tends to decline either immediately or after an initial stage of increasing returns; (b) the total production increases at first, but ultimately declines as the excessive supply of the variable factor hampers the functioning of the fixed factors.

Interpretation of the principle. The principle should be interpreted carefully. It refers to physical combinations of factors of production and to output of physical products. It throws no direct light on the profit or economic returns; however, as we shall see in the next chapter, economic returns conform closely to physical output.

After reading the above discussion, do not jump to the conclusion that output always decreases and never increases with an added application of a production factor. An early stage of increasing output may occur. This point will be discussed in connection with Table VIII (page 101), covering a situation where a third peck of wheat seed per acre increases the yield more than the second.

The second part of the principle should not be overlooked. Total output may continue to increase long after diminishing returns have set in. Continued applications of fertilizer may keep on increasing the total yield, although the amount of increase from each application becomes smaller each time.

The *total yield* begins to decrease only after such heavy applications of the variable element that it has become harmful rather than helpful. In planting corn we would expect but little difference in yield with two or three stalks per hill. If four grains were planted per hill, we would expect some decline in yield, and still smaller returns from five or six grains. With fertilizer or number of cultivations we might go much further than the usual farm practice before any actual decrease in yield occurred, although the added applications might not cause any noticeable increase.

Diminishing outputs with application of fertilizer. This principle may be illustrated by means of the figures in Table VI. Suppose we had eight plots, of one acre each, to be planted in potatoes. To the first plot we apply no fertilizer. To the second we apply 300 pounds of fertilizer. The third receives 600 pounds, the fourth 900 pounds, and so on up to 2,100 pounds on plot 8. It is likely that the yield will vary about as shown in column (3). The first few applications of fertilizer bring large increases in yield. After several applications, however, we find the increases in yield becoming smaller and small-

TABLE VI

DIMINISHING OUTPUT FROM VARIOUS AMOUNTS OF FERTILIZER

(Hypothetical Data)

(1) Plot Number	(2) Fertilizer (lb.)	(3) Total Yield (bu.)	(4) Additional Yield (bu.)
1	0	80	..
2	300	150	70
3	600	210	60
4	900	260	50
5	1,200	285	25
6	1,500	300	15
7	1,800	300	0
8	2,100	290	−10

er, until finally there is so much fertilizer on the land that no further increase occurs. In the illustration the plot receiving 1,800 pounds of fertilizer produces the same yield as the one with 1,500 pounds.

It is even possible that so much fertilizer might be applied that the last applications would actually decrease instead of increase yields. This is illustrated by plot 8, which yields only 290 bushels after 2,100 pounds of fertilizer have been applied, as contrasted with plot 7, which yield 300 bushels with 1,800 pounds.

Diminishing Total Yields and Diminishing Additional Yields

A distinction should be made between changes in *total* yield and changes in *additional* yield.   In Table VI, the total yields are shown in column (3) and the additional yields are shown in column (4).   On plot number 2 the

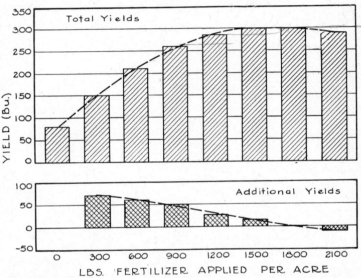

Fig. 14.—Hypothetical variation in yield of potatoes with added applications of fertilizer.

total yield is 150 bushels.   This represents an addition of 70 bushels over the yield on plot 1, which was obtained without fertilizer.   Increasing the fertilizer to 600 pounds on plot 3 results in an additional yield of 60 bushels over plot 2.   This amount gives a total yield of 210 bushels.

Notice that the *total* yield continues to increase up to plot 6.   The *additional* yields become smaller with each increase in the amount of fertilizer used.   After plot 6, the additional yield becomes zero on plot 7 and changes to a negative value on plot 8.

In Fig. 14, the total and the additional yields are shown in graphic form. Comparison of the two parts of this figure will show that the *additional* yield columns, shown at the bottom of the graph, represent simply the differences in height from one *total* yield column to the next.

TABLE VII

VARIATIONS IN YIELD OF CORN WITH ADDED
CULTIVATIONS

(1) Number of Times Cultivated	(2) Total Yield (bu.)	(3) Additional Yield (bu.)
0	8	..
1	27	19
2	38	11
3	44	6
4	48	4
5	51	3
6	52	1
7	50	−2

If there were a large number of plots and very small increases in amount of fertilizer from one plot to the next, the tops of the columns in Fig. 14 would approach a smooth curve instead of approximating the outline of a set of stairs. This is often referred to as the *curve of increasing and diminishing output.*

Increase and decrease from added cultivations of corn. Table VII shows the approximate way in which yields of corn increase and later decrease with added cultivations. The first cultivations result in large increases in yield. After this period, further cultivations have less effect.

Finally, if many unneeded cultivations are added, the yield will probably decrease because of accidental injuries to the plants or cultivating too late in the season.

Period of increasing returns. Can the second application of fertilizer or the second cultivation increase the yield even more than the first, so that the curve of output will rise for awhile before it begins to fall? This seldom

TABLE VIII

DIMINISHING OUTPUT FROM VARYING AMOUNTS OF
WHEAT SEED

(1) Seed per Acre (pk.)	(2) Total Yield (bu.)	(3) Additional Yield (bu.)	(4) Average Yield per Peck of Seed (bu.)	(5) Acres of Land per Peck of Seed
1	5.0	..	5.0	1.00
2	10.8	5.8	5.4	.50
3	17.3	6.5	5.8	.33
4	22.7	5.4	5.7	.25
5	25.7	3.0	5.1	.20
6	26.1	.4	4.4	.16
7	25.1	·1.0	3.6	.14
8	23.1	−2.0	2.9	.12

happens with the application of fertilizer, but it may occur with a small number of cultivations or with a small application of seed.

The tendency is illustrated in column (3) of Table VIII. Here the second peck of wheat seed increases the yield 5.8 bushels over that obtained from the first peck. If the land is very weedy, the first peck of seed is likely to produce such a thin stand that the wheat will be choked by weeds. But a somewhat thicker stand may enable the wheat to keep down the weeds and give more than a proportionate increase in yield. Thus the third peck of seed in Table VIII increases the yield by 6.5 bushels.

After a certain amount of seed has been applied (the third peck in Table VIII), the wheat plants begin to crowd one another and to use up the available plant food and soil moisture before the crop is matured. After this point each additional peck of seed gives a smaller *additional* yield than the preceding peck.[1] If an extremely

---

[1] We have discussed the curve of increasing and diminishing *additional* yields and the curve of *total* yields. A third curve is represented by column (4) of Table VIII. This is the *curve of average yields*.

Suppose that the wheat were a new and very valuable variety. In that case it would be desirable to secure the highest possible yield per peck of seed rather than per acre of land. This would mean that the grower should watch the curve of *average* yield rather than the curve of *additional* yield.

This case is, in some important respects, quite different from the ones just discussed. The curve of *total* and that of *additional* yield in Table VIII refer to the output per acre of land with varying applications of seed. The curve of *average* yield refers to the yield per peck of seed *with varying applications of land per unit of seed.*

It may seem strange at first to speak of varying the proportions of land, but this is because we usually think of land as existing in a fixed amount. Of course, land is fixed in the total, but there is no particular limit to the amount which an individual farmer can rent or buy from his neighbor. We often hear of a farmer who, having decided that his farm is too small to keep him busy, buys an additional 80 acres. He is simply increasing the proportion of land which he is combining with his labor and management.

If we compare columns (1) and (5) in Table VIII, starting at the bottom of the table, we see that the expression "8 pecks of seed per acre" may be turned around and stated as ".12 acre of land per peck of seed." "Seven pecks of seed per acre" may be expressed as ".14 acre of land per peck," and so on. Now, in columns (4) and (5), we see that increasing the amount of land per peck of seed results in higher (*average*) yields per peck of seed until a certain point is reached. Thus, with .12 acre of land per peck, the yield amounts to 2.9 bushels per peck of seed. With .14 acre per peck, a yield of 3.6 bushels per peck is secured, and so on. The highest yield per peck of seed is obtained with .33 acre of land per peck.

We secure the highest output of grain per unit of seed when we use a relatively large amount of *land* (.33 acre) per peck of seed. On the other hand, we obtain the highest output per acre of land when a relatively large amount of *seed* (6 pecks) is used per acre. Note that the output falls off if we apply too much land per unit of seed, just as the output declined when we applied too much seed per acre of land.

TABLE IX

CHANGES IN YIELD OF WHEAT WITH VARYING APPLICATIONS OF BOTH SEED AND FERTILIZER

(1)	(2)	(3)	(4)	(5)	(6)	(7)	(8)	(9)
		TOTAL YIELD IN BUSHELS				ADDITIONAL YIELD IN BUSHELS		
Pounds of Fertilizer	0	200	400	600	0	200	400	600
Pecks of Seed per Acre								
1	5.0	4.8	4.6	4.5	..	..	..	..
2	10.8	10.7	10.8	10.7	5.8	5.9	6.2	6.2
3	17.3	17.5	17.9	18.1	6.5	6.8	7.1	7.4
4	22.7	24.8	25.9	26.3	5.4	7.3	8.0	8.2
5	25.7	30.8	34.3	34.9	3.0	6.0	8.4	8.6
6	26.1	33.8	40.3	43.9	.4	3.0	6.0	9.0
7	25.1	34.3	43.1	49.9	−1.0	.5	2.8	6.0
8	23.1	33.5	43.8	52.3	−2.0	−.8	.7	2.4

large amount of seed is applied, even the total yield will begin to decline.

Variation in More Than One Element at a Time

By this time the question has probably been raised: What are the results if two or more elements are varied at the same time? Suppose, for instance, that we have

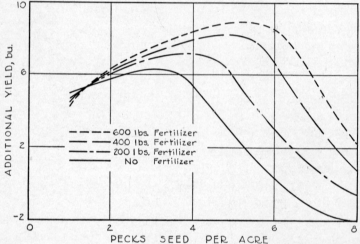

Fig. 15.—Changes in additional yield with varying applications of seed and fertilizer.

four fields: to one we apply no fertilizer, and to each of the other three we apply 200, 400, and 600 pounds of fertilizer, respectively, as shown in Table IX. Next, assume that we divide each of these four fields into eight plots and sow varying amounts of seed, from one to eight pecks, on each of these. What would be the variation in yield?

Naturally the problem becomes more complex as we

increase the number of variable factors, but the results will generally be approximately those shown in Table IX and in graphic form in Figure 15.

Notice, in Table IX, that the point of greatest yield per additional peck of seed is higher when 400 pounds of fertilizer are applied than when 200 pounds are used, and that it is higher with 600 pounds of fertilizer than with 400.

Another important point is that the application of more fertilizer not only leads to higher additional output per peck of seed but also causes the yield to continue to respond to additional seed longer than it would without the fertilizer. With 200 pounds of fertilizer the point of highest additional output is with 4 pecks of seed; with 400 pounds of fertilizer the maximum is with 5 pecks; and with 600 pounds it is with 6 pecks.

In such a case as this, we may find that additional fertilizer with a very light application of seed might lead to smaller rather than larger yields. The fertilizer also stimulates the growth of weeds. If the stand of wheat is very thin, more fertilizer may cause the weeds to choke the wheat worse than if little or no fertilizer had been applied. As more seed is applied and the wheat becomes thicker on the ground, the wheat tends to choke out weeds and the full benefit of the fertilizer goes to the wheat.

Wide Application of Diminishing Output

The principle of increasing and diminishing output may, at first, seem abstract or theoretical, but it is one of the most important principles with which we have to deal. It affects the amount of production in each enterprise, and may manifest itself in several ways in a single project.

Examples of its application may be observed in a great many sets of farm data.[2]

The same principle of diminishing output operates when we increase the size of a business managed by one man. It functions when we feed varying amounts of protein supplements per bushel of corn to fattening livestock. It is important in other businesses as well as in farming. It operates in factories when each man is given more machines to tend, or when the speed of an automobile assembly line is increased. It applies in stores when

---

[2] The table below contains one of many possible illustrations of the application of the principle of diminishing outputs which might be obtained from farm accounting material. These data were obtained from 1,300 Iowa farm records in 1929 and 1930. They show how acreages of corn varied on farms using different amounts of labor. It is hard to keep several men employed efficiently on a farm. The more men there are, the less effectively they are likely to work. Increasing the amount of labor per farm from 13 to 18 months in the course of a year was accompanied by an 18-acre increase in the corn raised. Increasing the labor by another 5 months was accompanied by a 17-acre increase in corn. By the time 33 months of labor were employed, 5 added months increased the corn by only 11 acres.

VARIATIONS IN ACREAGE OF CORN RAISED WITH INCREASING AMOUNTS OF LABOR

(Smoothed Trend Values from Iowa Farm Records, 1929 and 1930)

Months of Labor Used[a]	Total Acres of Corn	Additional Acres of Corn
8	23	..
13	43	20
18	61	18
23	78	17
28	94	16
33	107	13
38	119	11
43	126	8

[a] Mid-values of the respective groups.

additional clerks are employed in a single department. Although the principle is clearly a physical one, in the next chapter we shall see that it has very important economic consequences.

References

Black, John D., and Black, A. G., *Production Organization,* Holt, New York, 1926., Chapter V.

Gray, L. C., *Introduction to Agricultural Economics,* Macmillan, New York, 1924, Chapter X.

Holmes, C. L., *Economics of Farm Organization and Management,* Heath, Boston, 1928, Chapter XII.

Taylor, H. C., *Outlines of Agricultural Economics,* Macmillan, New York, 1925, Chapter XII.

U.S. Department of Agriculture, Department Bulletin **1277:** "Input as Related to Output in Farm Organization and Cost-of-Production Studies," by H. R. Tolley, J. D. Black, and M. J. B. Ezekiel, 1924.

CHAPTER VIII

The Principle of Diminishing Economic Returns

The Problem: To what extent is it profitable to increase one of a group of economic factors of production? How far down the curve of diminishing output is it advisable to go in applying fertilizer or labor? Where is the point of greatest profit? Is the highest profit point affected by product prices or by costs of the factors of production?

What is the Point of Highest Profit?

In the last chapter we found that, when the amount of one economic factor is increased, the physical output per unit of that factor sooner or later tends to decline. Now let us go back to the question of where it will *pay* to stop applying the fertilizer or labor, or whatever the variable factor may be.

Let us use for our illustration the figures given in Table VII. In this case the highest *additional* yield of corn is obtained with the first cultivation, but the highest *total* yield with the sixth. How many cultivations will bring the greatest financial returns? Will it pay to stop after the first cultivation? after the sixth? or at some point different from either of them?

Costs of raising the crop. In determining this point, we shall find that much depends on the market price of the crop. The point of highest profit also changes with the

costs of the factors of production.   Let us suppose that
a laborer together with the use of a team and cultivator
costs $1.30 per hour.   For the sake of simplicity we
shall assume that it requires an hour to cultivate an acre.
Other expenses—seed, preparing the seed bed, and harvesting the corn—amount to $10 per acre.

At these rates, if the corn is raised with one cultivation,
it will cost $11.30 per acre.   With two cultivations, it will
cost $12.60.   Three cultivations will bring the expense up
to $13.90, as shown in Table X.

Diminishing Additional Returns

Table X shows that the additional returns decline as
more cultivations are added.   Each cultivation adds $1.30
to the cost of raising the crop.   The added physical output is shown in column (3), and the value of this output
at 40 cents per bushel is indicated in column (8).

The first cultivation increases the yield by 19 bushels,
worth $7.60.   When we deduct from this $1.30, the cost
of cultivation, we find that the first cultivation increases
the returns by a net amount of $6.30.

The second cultivation further increases the yield by 11
bushels, worth $4.40.   When the added cost of $1.30 is
deducted, we find that the net return from the second cultivation is $3.10.

In similar calculations, we find that the net return from
the third cultivation is $1.10, and that from the fourth is
only 30 cents.

Marginal Net Returns

Notice that the *marginal returns* (or the highest total
net returns) do not occur at the vanishing point of addi-

Table X

VARIATION IN TOTAL RETURNS WITH DIFFERENT NUMBERS OF CULTIVATIONS

(1) Number of Times Cultivated	(2) Total Yield (bu.)	(3) Additional Yield (bu.)	(4) Total Expense	(5) Value of Crop @ 40¢ per bu.	(6) Total Net Return per Acre Land	(7) Net Return per Cultivation	(8) Value of Additional Yield @ 40¢ per bu.	(9) Net Return from Additional Cultivation
0	8	..	$10.00	$ 3.20	$ -6.80	..	..	..
1	27	19	11.30	10.80	-.50	$ -.50	$7.60	$6.30
2	38	11	12.60	15.20	2.60	1.30	4.40	3.10
3	44	6	13.90	17.60	3.70	1.17	2.40	1.10
4	48	4	15.20	19.20	4.00	1.00	1.60	.30
5	51	3	16.50	20.40	3.90	.78	1.20	-.10
6	52	1	17.80	20.80	3.00	.50	.40	-.90
7	50	-2	19.10	20.00	.90	.13	-.80	-2.10

tional physical output.   The fifth cultivation, in this illustration, adds 3 bushels to the yield.   But, with corn at 40 cents per bushel, this increase is worth only $1.20 while the cost of the added cultivation is $1.30.   The point of marginal returns is between the fourth and fifth cultivations, even though the fifth and sixth cultivations add small amounts to the physical yield.

Where should the farmer stop cultivating?   Each cultivation up to and including the fourth, increases the value of the product by more than the cost of cultivation. Thus each of these four cultivations increases the total net return from the crop.   The fifth cultivation, however, diminishes the net return by 10 cents.   The farmer should, therefore, cultivate the fourth time but not the fifth.

Between the fourth and fifth cultivations we reach the *margin* of returns from additional cultivation—that is, the point where the returns just barely cover the cost of the last bit of cultivation.   The cultivation applied up to this point has increased the total net returns.   However, any cultivation past this point increases the cost more than the income.

The application of labor or capital which results in an income just equal to the cost of applying it is known as the *marginal application*.   The returns from this unit of cultivation (or seed or fertilizer or labor, as the case may be) are called the *marginal returns*.

The marginal cultivation itself does not increase the *total net returns* from the crop.   But each earlier cultivation increases the total net returns and any cultivation after this point *decreases the returns*.   Therefore we may say that the point of *marginal* cultivation coincides with the point of highest *total* net returns.

The upper portion of Fig. 16 shows how the total value of the crop varies with different numbers of cultivations. The lower portion of Fig. 16 may help to follow through the changes in the total net returns.

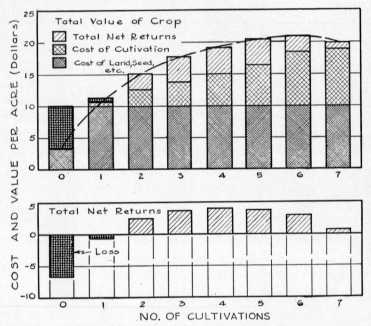

Fig. 16.—Variation in total net returns with different numbers of cultivations.

Lowest Cost per Bushel Does Not Necessarily Give Highest Net Return

An attempt is sometimes made to decide, by the use of figures on cost per unit of product, where to stop applying a factor of production (such as labor). It is often said, incorrectly, that the crop should be grown at the lowest average cost per bushel. This may occasionally be true

Table XI

VARIATIONS IN COST PER BUSHEL CONTRASTED WITH NET RETURNS PER ACRE

(1) Number of Times Cultivated	(2) Total Yield (bu.)	(3) Total Value @ 40¢ per bu.	(4) Extra Expense	(5) Average Cost per Bushel	(6) Cost per Added Bushel	(7) NET RETURNS PER ACRE Corn @ 40¢ per bu.	(8) NET RETURNS PER ACRE Corn @ 50¢ per bu.
0	8	$ 3.20	$10.00	$1.250	....	−$6.80	−$6.00
1	27	10.80	11.30	.418	$.068	−.50	2.20
2	38	15.20	12.60	.331	.118	2.60	6.40
3	44	17.60	13.90	.316	.217	3.70	8.10
4	48	19.20	15.20	.314	.325	4.00	8.80
5	51	20.40	16.50	.324	.433	3.90	9.00
6	52	20.80	17.80	.342	.130	3.00	8.20
7	50	20.00	19.10	.382	....	.90	5.90

—but only by coincidence. The correct statement is that it is most profitable to stop at the point of marginal cost per additional bushel, that is, where the last bushel costs as much as it is worth.

In Table X, it is shown that the *cost per added bushel increases as the returns per added cultivation decline.* The first cultivation increases the yield by 19 bushels. At a cost of $1.30 per cultivation, this means a cost of $.068 per bushel. By the time the sixth cultivation is added, the increase in yield is only one bushel. This bushel, therefore, costs $1.30.

In Table XI, column (6) shows that the 4 bushels added by the fourth cultivation cost $.325 per bushel. Since the corn is worth $.40, this cultivation adds to the net income. The fifth cultivation adds 3 bushels, which therefore cost $.433 per bushel, or 3.3 cents more than the corn is worth.

The first few cultivations lower the *average* cost per bushel by spreading the fixed costs per acre ($10 in this case) over a larger number of bushels. Later, as the returns begin to diminish more rapidly, the average cost per bushel begins to increase. This is shown in column (5) of Table XI.

Under the assumptions of this illustration, it happens that both the *lowest average cost* and the *marginal cost* occur with the fourth cultivation (or, more accurately, between the fourth and the fifth). The location of *marginal cost* depends partly, however, on the price per unit of the product. If the price of corn were raised to 50 cents, the point of marginal cost would then be between the fifth and sixth cultivations. The *lowest average cost* would still occur with the fourth cultivation, whereas the *highest net return per acre* would be obtained with the fifth.

Should a farmer try to get the *highest value of crops per acre?* Evidently not. The crop which results from six cultivations, as shown in Table X, is of greater total value than that from four. But the increases from the fifth and sixth cultivations were less than the cost of obtaining them. With six cultivations the farmer would realize a net return of only $3 per acre, in contrast with the $4 which he would get from four cultivations.

Statement of the Principle of Diminishing Returns

The principle of increasing and diminishing returns can now be stated in a form similar to that of the principle of increasing and diminishing output:

When one of a group of factors of production is increased in proportion to the others: (*a*) the returns per unit of the variable element tend to decline, either immediately or after an initial stage of increasing returns; (*b*) the total returns increase at first, but ultimately decline as the excessive supply of the variable factor hampers the functioning of the fixed factors.

Highest Returns per Acre versus Highest Returns per Cultivation

Would the farm renter find it profitable to cultivate his land as much as does the farm owner? For the purposes of comparison, let us make the differences between these two men as sharp and definite as possible. We shall assume that the renter has a rather limited supply of equipment, labor, and power, but can rent as large or as small a farm as he wants, and that the owner lives in a thickly settled area on a relatively small farm and cannot obtain more land. How will the theory we have just been discussing help us to settle this problem?

We have said that a farmer (if he has an ample supply of labor and equipment) should continue to add cultivations as long as the value of the increases in yield is more than the cost of added cultivation. The net returns per acre continue to increase up to the point of marginal returns from cultivation. In Table X and in Fig. 17, this

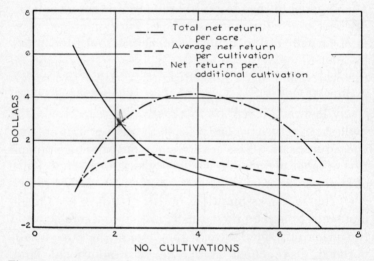

Fig. 17.—Comparison of net returns per acre with net returns per cultivation—corn at 40 cents per bushel.

point is reached between the fourth and fifth cultivations, since the increased yield from the fourth cultivation is worth 30 cents more than the cost of cultivation.

Does the point of marginal returns from cultivation also yield the highest average return per cultivation? A moment's thought will show that it does not.

This conclusion is illustrated by a comparison of the

curves in Fig. 17. In this case the highest average net return per cultivation is obtained from the *second* cultivation. See column (6), Table X. It is not obtained from the *fourth*. After the second cultivation the *average net return per cultivation* declines. But as long as the net return *from an additional cultivation* is anything greater than zero, the cultivation increases the net return per acre.

Now let us go back to the problem of the farm owner as compared to the renter. If the farm owner has plenty of labor and equipment available but cannot get more land, he will need to secure the highest net return per acre in order to make the largest net income. The tenant, on the other hand, has a limited supply of labor and equipment. If he lives where he can rent ample land at a relatively low rate, it will be to his advantage to obtain the highest net return per cultivation, that is, per unit of labor and equipment. This involves a more sparing application of labor per acre or, conversely, a more extensive use of land per laborer.

Of course, the assumptions in this case have been made more inflexible than they usually are, since the tenant and the owner of a small farm, if they live in the same neighborhood, have equal ability to rent additional land. Nevertheless, the principle is important. Insofar as a farmer with plenty of labor and capital really *is* limited in the amount of land available to him, to that extent will he need to secure the highest net return per acre. On the other hand, any farmer who has or can obtain the use of ample land, while his supply of labor is limited, will need to secure the highest net return per unit of labor rather than of land.

Point of Marginal Returns Changes with Prices

Suppose the price of corn should change. Would this factor change the number of cultivations that it would be profitable to apply? If, for example, as is shown in Table XII, the price of corn falls to 30 cents, it takes 4⅓ bushels of corn to realize $1.30. Since the fourth cultivation produces only 4 bushels, with corn at 30 cents we would find it profitable to stop with the third cultivation. The fourth is profitable only when the price is 40 cents. On the other hand, if corn goes up to 50 cents, it will be profitable to cultivate a fifth time. This will add 3 bushels of corn worth $1.50, while the cost of the cultivation is still $1.30.

Evidently, then, the most profitable place to stop cultivating is not determined in advance by some physical principle but depends on the price of the product. *The higher the price, the more cultivation it is profitable to apply.*

Price changes in cost factors. The point of marginal return might also be changed by variations in the cost rates. If the cost of a cultivation is $1 instead of $1.30, it will pay to add the fourth cultivation with corn at 30 cents, or to add the fifth if corn brings 40 cents.

If the price of one cost factor rose while others remained as before, farmers would use that factor more sparingly. For example, if wages alone increased, farmers would plan to use labor more sparingly—perhaps by the addition of larger-scale machinery.

Higher rents with labor at the same level would cause a more careful and more intensive use of land. The proportions of the production factors would be changed to include relatively more labor and less land per farm. If

TABLE XII

CHANGES IN ADDITIONAL RETURNS AT DIFFERENT PRICES OF CORN

(1) No. of Cultivations	(2) Cost per Added Cultivation	(3) Additional Yield per Acre (bu.)	(4) CORN AT 30¢ PER BUSHEL Value of Added Yield	(5) CORN AT 30¢ PER BUSHEL Added Return	(6) CORN AT 40¢ PER BUSHEL Value of Added Yield	(7) CORN AT 40¢ PER BUSHEL Added Return	(8) CORN AT 50¢ PER BUSHEL Value of Added Yield	(9) CORN AT 50¢ PER BUSHEL Added Return
1	$1.30	19	$5.70	$4.40	$7.60	$6.30	$9.50	$8.20
2	1.30	11	3.30	2.00	4.40	3.10	5.50	4.20
3	1.30	6	1.80	.50	2.40	1.10	3.00	1.70
4	1.30	4	1.20	− .10	1.60	.30	2.00	.70
5	1.30	3	.90	− .40	1.20	− .10	1.50	.20
6	1.30	1	.30	−1.00	.40	− .90	.50	− .80
7	1.30	−2	− .60	−1.90	− .80	−2.10	−1.00	−2.30

119

the interest rate should fall at the same time, the farmer would probably buy some additional piece of equipment which he had previously considered unprofitable because of its high price.

Variation in More Than One Factor at a Time

By studying the curve of diminishing returns for each of the respective factors, can you determine the proper amount of each production factor to use? Obviously not, because each factor cannot vary in the same direction at the same time. If we *increase* the proportion of labor to land in a certain enterprise, we are necessarily *decreasing* the proportion of land to labor.

The principle of diminishing returns is extremely important because it describes the way in which returns actually vary with changes in the proportion of any one factor. It can be used in the simple form described above only in deciding those problems which involve changes in only one factor at a time—for example, the proportion of horses to laborers to use in a certain farm operation. Or, it might determine the amount of seed to sow per acre, or the amount of feed for hogs or cows, or the amount of labor that it is worth while to spend on cows or hogs.

Even the questions just mentioned will eventually involve more than the one simple proportion. Suppose we had decided that plowing could be done most economically with a six-horse team and a gang plow, and then discovered that we had no other work which required more than five horses. The greatest economy in one direction might be more than offset by a loss in another.

Our problem is to organize the most profitable farm business possible. This business is made up of the four

factors of production.   Which of these can be varied and
which must remain constant?

Variable factors of production.   If the supply of one
of the factors of production is really fixed, this allows us
to use the method we have been discussing (that of variable returns) to fit the other factors to it.   Which factors
really are fixed and which are variable?·   Land and buildings are usually considered a fixed type of factor, whereas
the amounts of feeds, fertilizers, machinery, and labor
can be increased or decreased at will.   Of course, buying
land and buildings does require a greater outlay of capital,
but it is not necessary to buy the land.   An additional 40
or 80 acres can usually be rented somewhere in the neighborhood.   Since some of the capital for new buildings
can be borrowed, these two elements are not necessarily
fixed in amount.

Labor is sometimes said to be the factor most nearly
fixed in the supply available to an individual farmer.
But a good hired man can usually be employed if the
farmer is willing to pay enough for him.   The real problem here is again related to the principle of diminishing returns.   Would the extra laborer add more to the farm income than his wages add to the expense?

Some farmers can keep two or three men working profitably.   Others find that they cannot keep one man working efficiently enough to earn his wages.   In the latter
case the real limitation on the amount of hired labor
comes from a limited capacity for management on the
part of the farmer.

This observation suggests that the fixed factor of production may really be management, rather than land,
capital, or labor.   In varying the factors of production,
the farmer usually develops a combination which he finds

most economical under his particular conditions. Next, if he is to secure maximum returns, he will try to expand or contract the size of his organization until he has reached the size of business that is best for his ability as a manager. Not only must he fit to each other his land, capital, and labor, but he must also fit his organization to his managerial ability.

Courtesy John Deere Co.

Fig. 18.—The amount of fertilizer or lime to use involves a problem of diminishing returns.

Wide Application of the Principle

We find the principle of increasing and diminishing returns operating in every phase of farming. Whenever we increase the amount of a variable factor of production that is used in combination with fixed amounts of the other factors, we find that the returns per unit of the variable factors tend to decline, even though they have first gone through a stage of increase. This is true regardless of whether the variable factor is the amount of labor used on a certain acreage of land, or the amount of fertilizer applied per acre. It is equally true with the amount of power used per man, the amount of liquid capi-

TABLE XIII

VARIATIONS IN RETURNS FROM LIVESTOCK WITH
INCREASES IN ACREAGE OF FARMS
(Smoothed trend values from Iowa Farm Records, 1929 and 1930)

TOTAL ACRES IN FARM	VALUES OF SMOOTHED TREND	
	Total Livestock Income	Additional Livestock Income
80	$2600	. . .
120	3000	$400
160	3550	550
200	4200	650
240	4875	675
280	5500	625
320	6050	550
360	6500	450
400	6800	300

tal kept on hand, or the amount of land and labor managed by a single farm operator.

Many illustrations of the application of this principle could be given. Successive cultivations of corn have been used in this chapter. Another application, also derived from farm records, is shown in Table XIII, covering the variations in income from livestock, with increases in the acreage of land, in a group of 1,300 farm records in 1929 and 1930.

On these farms about 85 percent of the farm income was from the sale of livestock or livestock products. Usually the amount of labor increases as the amount of land increases—at least up to 280 acres. In these cases, up to the 240-acre size of farm each added 40 acres of land resulted in a greater additional return from livestock products. After this point, each added 40 acres brought in a smaller *additional return*. Also, the *total returns* increased more and more slowly on the larger farms when the amount of land was increased more than the labor.

References

Black, John D., and Black, A. G., *Production Organization*, Holt, New York, 1926, Chapter VI.

Gray, L. C., *Introduction to Agricultural Economics*, Macmillan, New York, 1924, Chapter X.

Holmes, C. L., *Economics of Farm Organization and Management*, Heath, Boston, 1928, Chapters XI and XII.

Taylor, H. C., *Outlines of Agricultural Economics*, Macmillan, New York, 1925, Chapter XII.

Minnesota Bulletin 205: "A Study of Farm Organization in Southwestern Minnesota," by George A. Pond and Jesse W. Tapp, 1923.

U.S. Department of Agriculture, Department Bulletin 1277: "Input as Related to Output in Farm Organization and Cost-of-Production Studies," by H. R. Tolley, J. D. Black, and M. J. B. Ezekiel, 1924.

Part III

THE CROP SYSTEM

CHAPTER IX

Selection of the Crops

The Problem: How shall the farmer plan a budget for the crop system? What information should he include in it? Where shall he get this information?

Choosing Between Alternative Crops

How can the farmer choose between alternative crops? Let us suppose that a farmer has decided his oat crop is not sufficiently profitable. Would it pay to plant barley instead of oats? How can he determine which crop would bring the greater return?

Since the planting and the harvesting of these two crops occur at about the same times, the problem is easier. The labor and power requirements are very similar. There will be some difference in the costs of seed, threshing, and twine, as well as in the returns from them. If oats are planted, expenses will be approximately as follows:

Expected yield on 30 acres @ 40 bu. per acre, or 1,200 bu. @ 35¢..$420.00
Direct outlay:
    Seed, 105 bu. @ 50¢...................... $52.50
    Twine, 90 lb. @ 12¢...................... 10.80
    Threshing, 1,200 bu. @ 2½¢.............. 30.00
Total direct outlay... 93.30
Value of crop over direct outlay.............................$326.70

The corresponding figures for barley will be:

Expected yield on 30 acres @ 27 bu. per acre, or 810 bu. @ 55¢.. $445.50
Direct outlay:
    Seed, 68 bu. @ 75¢...................... $51.00
    Twine, 82 lb. @ 12¢...................... 9.84
    Threshing, 810 bu. @ 3¢.................. 24.30
Total direct outlay... 85.14
Value of crop over direct outlay............................$360.36
Advantage of barley over oats..............................$ 33.56

This illustration shows how to use the budgetary
method of choosing farm projects. In the case described, it may not be necessary to consider any enterprises other than the two under direct comparison.
This is one of the most simple budgeting problems,
however. If the choice had been between oats and
wheat, the problem of harvesting corn in the fall in time
to plant the wheat would have had to be considered. A
change from oats to wheat would also have meant a shift
from a feed to a cash crop; consequently the feed supply
would have been altered, and this would have affected
the livestock enterprises.

Estimating the probable returns from each of the alternative enterprises is the first step in the budgeting
process. Next we estimate the probable direct outlays.
Then we compare the net returns. *It is necessary to
consider only those elements of cost which would be
changed by planting one crop instead of the other.*

In comparing the returns from barley and oats, we
find that our budget did not take into account the factor
of labor. The reason was that the labor requirements
of the two crops are almost identical. Any items which
would change with the choice of crop should, of course,
be included. The practical farmer really uses the above

process of choice even though he may not put his figures down on paper.

Crop Budget Must Also Consider Livestock

According to our estimates, there is an advantage of about $33 in planting barley instead of oats. Is this enough information for us to change our crop system? Do the two crops fit in equally well with the livestock and other enterprises? The two grains are somewhat different in their feeding qualities. For what purposes are they being raised? The oats would be better for horses, dairy cows, and the breeding herd of hogs. Barley would probably be preferred for fattening stock. In a later section of this chapter we shall return to the relationships among the different enterprises.

How reliable is our basic information on yields, probable costs of seed and other supplies, and probable market price of each crop? If the oat yield turned out to be 44 bushels instead of 40, or the barley 24 bushels instead of 27, the oats might be slightly more advantageous. Or, if barley prices were 5 cents lower than our estimate, oats would still be more profitable. Where can we obtain reasonably dependable information on probable prices, yields, and amounts and values of seed, fertilizer, or other materials required?

Sources of Basic Data

Where can we secure satisfactory information on probable yields? Usually a farmer will have had some experience with at least one of the crops he is considering. Sometimes, however, the choice will be between an old crop and a new one, which has not yet been tried out in the neighborhood.

If the neighbors have raised the new crop, the farmer can use, as a basis for his computations, their results on similar land. If the new crop has not yet been raised in the neighborhood, he may find state or Federal reports on yields. He should be conservative in estimating his own yields from those of others, because it often takes two or three years to get a new crop well started.

In estimating materials needed in producing the crops, the farmer will have his own experience and that of his neighbors to serve as a guide. For new crops, he can use agricultural experiment station bulletins or standard texts on farm crops or livestock raising.

Estimating prices is a more difficult matter. We cannot use prices of the preceding year, because wide annual fluctuations generally occur. Too often farmers are influenced in their decisions by prices they received in the year just passed. This is particularly true of the potato crop. After a short crop, with corresponding high prices, too many potatoes will be planted and prices consequently drop. The man who plants his crops according to the prices of the preceding year is usually just a year behind and always out of step with the current situation.

The prices to consider are those which appear probable for the coming season. The agricultural outlook material which is made available annually by the United States Department of Agriculture is a great help. It summarizes what evidence there is on probable prices. Of course, the predictions cannot always be right, since many things can happen to upset the situation before the crop is actually marketed. Each farmer should study the outlook data, and then interpret them and other available information as they apply to his own plans.

If no satisfactory outlook material is at hand, an average of prices for a product for the past five years may often be used as a basis for the estimate. The present production and demand situations should be considered in connection with this average. In no case should data from past years be used without taking the present outlook into consideration.

The Complete Crop Budget

We are now ready to draw up the budget for the crop system of the entire farm. We have already considered most of the problems that will come up when we are working out such a budget.

Let us suppose that a young man who has had some farm experience in the neighborhood is about to start the operation of a quarter-section farm. He has in mind the four major requirements of the crop plan:

(1) The crop plan should yield the maximum net value of crops over a long period of years.

(2) It should maintain the soil fertility.

(3) It should make possible efficient use of cost elements, particularly of labor and power.

(4) It should fit in well with the requirements of the other enterprises, particularly with the feed requirements of livestock projects.

The farmer decides, after considering all these things, that a five-year rotation, corn-corn-oats-clover hay-pasture, would probably be best for his situation. He wants to outline this plan in definite, written form, in order to compare it with another plan he is considering, and also to have it to serve as a guide if he should adopt it.

What information should be entered in the crop budget? First the farmer prepares a list of the crops and acreages to be planted in each. Then he must include an estimate of the expenses involved, and a plan for disposing of the crops after they are raised. Finally there should be estimates of yield and probable value of the crops.

Form of the crop budget. The result will be something like the form shown on page 133. At the top of this form the rotation to be followed is stated clearly, since this item explains the relative acreages of the different crops.

In column (1) is written the name of each crop, and in column (2) the acreage to be planted to each in order to carry out the rotation. In column (3) are direct expenses. Only actual cash outlays should be entered here. In column (4) is entered the amount to be purchased, and in column (5) the probable outlay for that item.

The expected yield in bushels or tons is entered in column (6). The disposition of the crops is accounted for in the remaining columns. From the livestock budget must be brought the estimated amounts of feed needed; these are entered in column (7). If the farmer raises his own seed, the amount to be kept for that purpose is placed in column (8). The quantity of crops to be sold is entered in column (9), and the expected receipts are shown in column (10). At the bottom of column (10) is shown the total income expected from the direct sale of crops.

It is possible to compute values of crops to be fed and kept for seed, but this complicates the budget and does not add to its usefulness. Since our purpose is to estimate the net farm income, the computation is not necessary.

Entering values of feed will not help us to determine how profitable our livestock projects are, because not all

Form A

Farm Budget Forms

THE CROP PLAN

Rotation: Corn—Corn—Oats—Hay—Pasture

(1) CROP	(2) ACRES	(3) DIRECT EXPENSES Kind	(4) DIRECT EXPENSES Amount	(5) DIRECT EXPENSES Value	(6) Expected Yield	(7) DISPOSITION OF CROPS Feed	(8) DISPOSITION OF CROPS Seed	(9) Sales Amount	(10) Sales Value
Corn..............	48	Seed Hail Ins.	10 bu.	$20.00 30.00	2,400 bu.	2,390 bu.	10 bu.		
Oats..............	24	Seed Twine Threshing Hail Ins.	80 bu. 60 lb.	42.00 8.00 18.00 12.00	960 bu.	880 bu.	80 bu.		
Hay, Clover, and Timothy.	24	Seed		35.00	30 tons	30 tons			
Pasture, Rotation..........	24								
Pasture, Permanent........	30								
Farmstead, Roads, etc.....	10								
Total..............	160			165.00					

133

feeds have a market value. The use of such products as corn stalks, which cannot be sold, and the utilization of available labor during slack seasons may be among the more important reasons for keeping some livestock enterprise. Any value figures given to such resources would be entirely arbitrary and misleading. They would seem to make possible a profit comparison of these enterprises, whereas such a comparison really depends upon the arbitrary values given and not on the real advantages or disadvantages which sheep, hogs, or dairy cows have in the organization of that specific farm.

The crop budget should be regarded as only one section of the entire farm budget, not as a complete plan; in fact, the crop plan we have just described may need to be revised somewhat after we have considered the livestock and other divisions of the farm plan.

The crop plan should be carefully designed to fit the rest of the farm. It should seldom be changed, since it must look ahead for several years. Its final success depends to a large extent on whether or not it will maintain or increase the productivity of the land. This does not mean that the crop plan should be forgotten as soon as it is put into effect. Even a long-time plan should be watched and checked up on from year to year. If a farmer is really going to make use of budgets and records, he should plan a convenient set of crop records. Planning such records will be discussed in Chapter X.

References

Hopkins, John A., *Farm Records*, Collegiate Press, Ames, Iowa, 1936, Chapter II.

Arkansas Bulletin 262: "Three Years' Study of Farm Management and Incomes in a Typical Upland Section," by J. A. Dickey, 1931.

Idaho Bulletin 188: "Planning the Farm Business for the Year Ahead," by Paul A. Eke and Ezra T. Benson, 1932.

Illinois Bulletin 329: "Organizing the Corn Belt Farm for Profitable Production," by H. C. M. Case, R. H. Wilcox, and H. A. Berg, 1929.

Kentucky Bulletin 274: "Man Labor, Horse Work and Materials Used in Producing Crops in Christian County," by J. B. Hutson and W. G. Finn, 1926.

Minnesota Bulletin 205: "A Study of Farm Organization in Southwestern Minnesota," by George A. Pond and Jesse W. Tapp, 1923.

Minnesota Bulletin 282: "An Economic Study of Crop Production in the Red River Valley of Minnesota," by George A. Pond, George A. Sallee, and C. W. Crickman, 1931.

South Dakota Bulletin 226: "Profitable Farming Systems for East Central South Dakota," by C. A. Bonnen and J. B. Hutson, 1927.

South Dakota Bulletin 249: "Economic Adjustments on Farms in Southeastern South Dakota," by R. H. Rogers, 1930.

U.S. Department of Agriculture, Farmers' Bulletin 1564: "Farm Budgeting," by J. B. Hutson, 1928.

U.S. Department of Agriculture, Farmers' Bulletin 1463: "Successful Farming on 160-Acre Farms in Central Indiana," by Lynn Robertson and H. W. Hawthorne, 1925.

CHAPTER X

Major and Minor Rotations and Crop Records

The Problem: What is a satisfactory rotation? Is it necessary to follow a rotation, or can the crop system be shifted about from year to year? How can we measure results of the crop plan? What records should be kept? How are the forms properly drawn up?

Advantages of a Rotation

Is it necessary to follow a rotation? Many farmers use only incomplete rotations or none at all. In the cash grain area of Iowa, a common procedure is to alternate corn and oats, with a few acres out for pasture or hay. Sometimes a field is kept in corn for two or three years, and then changed to oats when the yield begins to suffer. Farmers using this system insist that it is the most convenient and produces the most grain. Are they mistaken when they conclude that they do not need a rotation? What benefits would they derive from a rotation?

The first advantage of a regular rotation is that it usually results in a greater total yield of crops *over a period of years*. If corn is grown continuously on the same land for three or four years, the yield will decline considerably. Different crops have somewhat different plant food requirements. By rotating the crops, it is possible to use the available plant food elements more evenly.

A second advantage is that the rotation makes it easier to build up the fertility of the soil or to keep it at a high level. Soil-building legume crops help to maintain the nitrogen in the soil, and it is possible to build up the organic content in the soil by plowing under green manure crops. It is much easier to follow a soil-building program if there is a regular rotation than if crops are varied in an irregular manner.

Third, the rotation helps control weed or insect pests. In order to do this effectively, the rotation should include at least one cultivated crop. Different crops occupy the land at somewhat different times of the year. Weeds that make seed early in the season are eradicated by the cultivation of corn, whereas those that mature late in the season are likely to be killed when the hay is cut at that phase of the rotation. Changing crops from year to year also prevents many insect pests from becoming a serious menace.

A fourth advantage of a rotation is that it may use labor more economically. When small grain is planted to follow corn, it is not necessary to plow for that crop. Discing is usually enough preparation. If clover or grass seed is planted with the small grain, a second preparation of the soil is saved.

A fifth advantage is that, in a well-chosen rotation, it is possible to make use of the land for the greater part of the year. When winter wheat follows corn, the wheat gets started the same year that the corn was raised. The following year the clover or grass planted in the wheat becomes established while the wheat is maturing.

The Major Rotation

The major rotation should be so planned that it will produce the greatest possible value of salable or usable crop material during a period of years. It should include the largest possible acreage of the crop that grows best and is most profitable in that locality. Allowance should

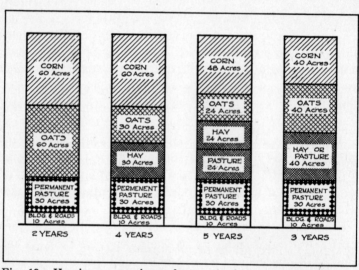

Fig. 19.—Varying proportions of crops in four rotations. 160-acre farm with 120 acres of crop land.

be made, of course, for maintaining soil fertility and using labor to the best advantage. In the corn belt, the rotation should contain a relatively large acreage of corn; in the cotton belt, as much cotton as possible should be included; and in the small grain belt, as much wheat or barley as possible. The harmful results of raising the same crop continuously may be avoided by not raising the crop too often in succession.

Figure 19 shows the various acreages of corn and other crops that will be raised in four different rotations on a quarter-section farm with 120 acres of crop land. The two-year alternation between oats and corn produces the largest proportion of grain, but the corn acreage is no larger than in the four-year rotation of corn-corn-small grain-hay. The four-year rotation is easier on the soil than the corn-oats combination, but neither of them should be used except on new or very rich land.

A third possibility for land which is comparatively fertile is the five-year rotation. This will produce 48 acres of corn instead of 60 acres, as in the two rotations noted above. Corn yields will be better maintained because some crop other than corn is grown on the land three years out of five. This rotation, or some modification of it, is common in dairy sections since it produces large amounts of hay and pasture for the cows. It will hardly do, however, if the principal livestock enterprise is not cattle, for then it would be difficult or impossible to use up the large amount of roughage.

For a poor soil or one that needs to be built up, the fourth rotation is likely to be the most profitable. This consists of one year of corn, one of small grains, and one of pasture or hay. Here there are 40 acres of corn in the 120 crop acres.

Obviously there are many other rotations or modifications. Each should be judged according to local conditions, the fertility of the land, and the requirements of profitable livestock enterprise for the community.

Minor Rotations

A major and a minor rotation can often be used to good advantage on the same farm. Small acreages are needed for hog pastures, truck patches, and so on.   Sometimes parts of main fields are used for these purposes. If this practice is not possible, these small acreages should be made into a minor rotation.   Minor crops will benefit from rotation just as major ones do.   Hog parasites can hardly be kept under control unless the hogs are shifted

Photo J. C. Allen and Son

Fig. 20.—Hog pastures can usually be fitted into a minor rotation.

occasionally to other ground, and the same situation holds for diseases or pests of truck crops.

It may be more expensive to use parts of the main fields for the small acreages than to fence off permanent acreages.   It would be necessary to put up temporary fences for hog pasture.   A permanently arranged minor rotation also allows better water and feeding facilities to be established than could usually be done if parts of main fields were used. The hog pasture may be one element in a minor rotation with the truck patch, potatoes, alfalfa, or other minor crops. The fields should be as convenient to the buildings as possible, especially if livestock are to be run in some of the fields.

Crop Records

Merely making a plan is not sufficient for successful farming; the plan must be carried out and changed whenever necessary. Several years may be required to put crop plans into full effect, and consequently it is difficult to measure progress on them. The weather each year causes a considerable amount of variation in results. Unless there are actual records over a period of years, it is very hard to tell how well the plan has succeeded and it may even be lost sight of entirely.

There are only a few items to be written down in the crop record each year. At the time, facts regarding yields or amounts of fertilizer used appear so obvious that it may seem unnecessary to write them down, and yet if they are not recorded in writing they are usually forgotten by the following year. It is, therefore, important that records be organized when the crop plan is adopted and that they be ready for use during subsequent seasons.

The Farm Map

One of the simplest and most useful records is the farm map, one type of which is shown in Fig. 21. The map has several important uses besides that of serving as a record. It will help greatly in planning improvements in farm layout. It may show up places where distances to fields could be shortened, fences straightened, and so on. It enables the farmer to visualize his farm as a whole. An accurate survey of the outside boundaries of the farm, if they are irregular, may be of great value in avoiding misunderstandings with neighbors.

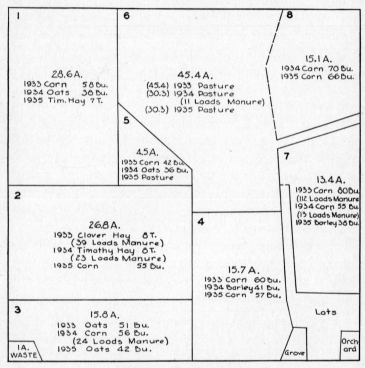

Fig. 21.—The farm map.

In making a farm map, although it is not necessary that the farm be actually surveyed, we find that all measurements must be carefully taken. Fields do not always have the acreage that the farmer believes they have. If a field that is assumed to contain 40 acres yields 1,600 bushels of corn, the yield could be considered only fair.

But if measurements prove that the field had only 36 acres, the yield of over 44 bushels may convince the farmer that his soil-building plan has really been effective.

Accurate information on yields makes it possible to compare the productivity of the different fields. Soils vary in their requirements for maintenance or increase of fertility; yet these differences do not show up clearly unless the data on the yields are accurately known.

The method by which the map is finally drawn up is not important. It should be neatly done, of course. A good plan is to make a map which can be mounted or tacked on the wall, and which is large enough to have the yields for several years written within the outline of each field. Another satisfactory arrangement is to have two or three small copies of a size that will fit into the farm account book. On one of these maps could be written soil treatments for several years, another could be used to record crop yields, and so on.

Even if the map each year includes only the yield and the crop for each field, a very useful record of productivity is gradually developed. The longer it is kept, the more highly it will be valued.

The Record Of Soil Treatment

The farm map may not have enough space available to enter a full record of the crop production and the soil treatment that each field has had. A more complete record may be kept somewhat as in the form shown on page 144. Any farmer who is trying to build up his soil will sooner or later find that he needs such a record. The crop yield alone does not tell the whole story; he must know, also, what fertilizer or manure was applied to the land, what legumes have been raised and turned under, whether the soil is sweet or acid, and so on.

Form B
Farm Budget Forms
CROP AND SOIL TREATMENT RECORD

FIELD NO.: 1 .... ACRES: 42
TOPOGRAPHY: Smooth .... SOIL: Loam

Year	Crop	Yield	Soil Treatment, Manure, Fertilizer
1931	Corn	43 bu.	Manure, 120 loads east half
1932	Corn	46 bu.	
1933	Oats	45 bu.	200 lb. acid phosphate per acre
1934	Red clover 20 acres Sweet clover 22 acres	1.8 tons Pastured	
1935	Corn	58 bu.	
1936	Corn	55 bu.	Manure, 150 loads on west half

FIELD NO.: 2 .... ACRES: 38.0
TOPOGRAPHY: Rolling .... SOIL: Clay Loam

Year	Crop	Yield	Soil Treatment, Manure, Fertilizer
1931	Oats	42 bu.	
1932	Corn	38 bu.	
1933	Corn	44 bu.	Manure, 190 loads
1934	Oats	47 bu.	250 lb. acid phosphate per acre
1935	Red clover 20 acres Sweet clover 18 acres	1.6 tons Pastured	
1936	Corn	51 bu.	

144

The farmer can know, with such a record as this, not only what immediate effect a certain application of fertilizer has on the yields of crops but also how long the effect lasts. He can compare the yields from such a field with those from a similar one that has been treated differently. This record requires only a small amount of work to keep and is extremely valuable because it helps to remove guesswork from the crop and soil program.

Measuring the amount of crop produced. To have accurate information on yields, it is as necessary to measure the amount of crop raised each year as to measure the size of the field. The former task is not difficult, within a reasonable margin of error, provided it is planned in advance.

If the crop from one field is not mixed with that from another in the crib or bin, the problem is simple. The farmer should know the capacities of his cribs, bins, and mows. It is necessary to take accurate measurements in figuring these capacities. If painted marks on one side of the cribs and mows indicate various depths, it will be easier to estimate amounts of grain or hay. The measurements of the wagon box in which corn is hauled should also be carefully ascertained.

Hay is the hardest crop to measure accurately, because the number of cubic feet required to make a ton varies widely. In order to have an approximate estimate of the yield of hay, it is a good idea to drive a load over the scales occasionally.

References

Hopkins, John A., *Farm Records*, Collegiate Press, Ames, Iowa, 1936, Chapters I and II.

Warren, G. F., *Farm Management*, Macmillan, New York, 1916, Chapter XIV.

CHAPTER XI

Requirements in Crop Production

The Problem: How much labor, horse work, seed, and similar cost elements are required to produce the more common farm crops?

General Requirements of Crop Production

In deciding on a rotation, the farmer should consider the requirements of the various crops for labor, power, fertilizer, and other cost elements, as well as their yields. Will there be enough labor and power available during the busy season to handle the rotation he is considering? Often a change in acreages may shift some of the peak labor requirements so that the farm will run more smoothly and produce better yields. Such planning may also make it possible to get along with less hired labor.

If the labor requirements of two or more crops conflict, it is necessary either to hire more labor or to neglect one of the crops. Extra labor may not be easy to find, and the farmer may try to hurry through the work on one crop while he postpones work on the other. This practice generally means poorer yields and less satisfactory results.

Corn Crop

Labor and power requirements of corn vary considerably in different parts of the United States. This variation is shown in Table XIV.   In Iowa, corn is raised in large fields with relatively large-capacity machinery. In New York, corn is raised in small and often rough fields.   In Iowa the crop is harvested by picking the ears from the standing stalks.   In New York, corn is generally cut and shocked, and then husked from the shocks.

TABLE XIV

SUMMARY OF REQUIREMENTS PER ACRE USED IN
RAISING CORN

	IOWA[a] 1927	NEW YORK[b] 1927-1930	MISSISSIPPI[c] 1927
Acres of Corn per Farm.......	46	3.7	9.8
Yield per Acre, bushels.......	43.4	29.5	22.5
Requirements in Growing:			
Seed, pounds.............	9.0[d]	17.5	7.8
Fertilizer, pounds..........	0	144	180
Labor, hours.............	10.3	25.2	32.5
Horse work, hours........	29.6	35.2	32.2
Tractor, hours.............	.1	2.8	.5
Labor Used in Harvesting:			
Labor, hours.............	6.6	33.4	9.7
Horse work, hours........	12.7	12.0	4.6
Total labor, hours........	17.0	58.6	42.2
Total horse work, hours ..	42.3	47.2	36.8

[a] From Iowa Bulletin 289, data for Cedar County.
[b] From mimeographed publication: "Results of Cost Accounts on Grain Crops," by J. F. Harriott and L. M. Vaughan, Cornell University, 1931.
[c] From Mississippi Bulletin 256.
[d] Approximately.

In Mississippi the leaves are stripped from the stalks by hand and tied in small bundles for forage.   Later the ears are picked from the stalks.

Labor used in growing corn for harvest.   With these different methods we should expect to find a wide variation in the amount of labor used.   On the farms studied,

TABLE XV

CULTURAL SEQUENCES—EFFECT ON YIELD AND LABOR REQUIREMENTS PER ACRE OF CORN

Sequence No.	Sequence				Yield per Acre		Labor Requirements per Acre		
	Number of Discings	Number of Harrowings	Number of Cultivations	Total Acres	Bushels	Rank	Man Hours	Horse Hours	Rank
1	2	2	3	1,522	40	5	4.2	14.4	4
2	2	2	4	1,341	40	5	5.0	16.8	8
3	2	1	3	1,168	35	8	3.9	13.2	3
4	2	3	3	915	41	4	4.5	15.6	5
5	2	3	4	687	49	1	5.3	18.0	9
6	2	1	4	629	43	3	4.7	15.6	6
7	1	1	3	674	35	8	3.3	10.8	1
8	2	4	3	596	39	6	4.8	16.8	7
9	1	2	3	502	38	7	3.6	12.0	2
10	1	3	3	398	46	2	3.9	13.2	3

over twice as much labor was used per acre in Mississippi in raising a crop of 22.5 bushels of corn as in raising 43.4 bushels in Iowa. In New York to produce a smaller

TABLE XVI

VARIATIONS IN LABOR REQUIREMENTS IN HARVESTING CORN

(From Michigan Special Bulletin 241, Ohio Bulletin 396, and Iowa Bulletin 289)

LABOR REQUIREMENTS	HOURS PER ACRE		
	Man Hours	Horse Hours	Tractor Hours
Cut by hand, husked from shock:			
Michigan	22.5	8.8	..
Ohio	23.6	5.6	..
Cut by binder, husked from shock:			
Ohio	21.0	10.0	..
Put into silo:			
Iowa	9.3	12.8	1.1
Michigan	10.8	11.6	.8
Cut by hand, husked by shredder:			
Ohio	20.0	13.7	..
Cut by binder, husked by shredder:			
Michigan	10.7	9.8	1.1
Ohio	17.4	18.3	..
Cut by binder, bundle fed without husking:			
Michigan	8.0	7.0	..
Picked from standing stalks by hand:			
Iowa	6.6	12.7	..
Michigan	8.5	16.9	..
Ohio	8.7	15.0	..
Picked from stalks by mechanical picker:			
Michigan (1-row pickers)	4.2	5.3	1.4
Iowa (2-row pickers)	1.6	1.6	.0

crop of 29.5 bushels, over three times as much labor was used as in Iowa. There is less difference in the amount of horse work per acre.

Even within a single state there are differences in methods of raising such a crop as corn. The weather and the condition of the soil are responsible for some of these, as well as the individual farmer's choice of method.

Table XV shows the ten most common sequences in raising and cultivating corn, as found in a study of corn production in seven Iowa counties in 1927.

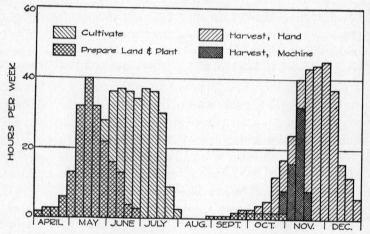

Fig. 22.—Seasonal distribution of labor on 40 acres of corn in Iowa. Data based on Iowa Bulletin 261.

The most common sequence consisted of two discings (one before and one after plowing), two harrowings (one before and one after planting), and three cultivations. The sequence which required the least labor (No. 7) consisted of one discing, one harrowing, and three cultivations. The highest yield came from sequence No. 5, with two discings, three harrowings, and four cultivations.

Labor requirements in harvesting corn. The wide variation in method of harvesting and in labor required is shown in Table XVI. In the eastern part of the country, corn is usually cut and shocked by hand, and then husked later. In Michigan this procedure required 22 or 23 hours of man labor and from 6 to 9 hours of horse work per acre. At the other extreme is the use of the 2-row mechanical picker which required, in Iowa, 1.6 hours of man labor, 1.6 hours of horse work, and .6 hours of tractor work.

Seasonal labor requirements for corn. The amount of labor needed for corn at different times in the season depends on the methods used and the size of the equipment available. Fig. 22 shows typical seasonal labor requirements in raising 40 acres of corn in Iowa. There are two busy seasons. From the middle of April to the end of May is a peak season for preparing the seedbed and planting. Cultivation begins during the second half of May and lasts until the middle of July. The second peak season occurs in the fall when the corn is harvested, and lasts approximately from the middle of October to the middle of December.

On farms from which the data in Fig. 22 were obtained, cultivation was done partly with 1-row and partly with 2-row cultivators. Most of the harvesting was done by picking the ears by hand from the standing stalks. A few farmers used mechanical pickers.

If 2-row cultivators had been used exclusively, the labor peak in June and July would have been one third to one quarter less. Four-row tractor cultivators could cut the labor to not over half that shown.

The use of a 2-row mechanical picker permits the crop to be harvested much earlier than it can be finished by hand. It requires only one third or one fourth as much labor. Unless it is used on a large acreage, however, the picker is likely to be too expensive an investment for one

farmer. But it may be owned co-operatively by two or
three farmers, or it may be hired out for custom work.

Oats and Barley

The labor requirements for raising oats and barley are
very similar. The principal difference is in the amount

Fig. 23.—Corn picking by hand.

of seed required per acre. On the farms studied in Iowa,
3.7 bushels of oats were used for seed, as compared with
2.7 bushels of barley. In New York, 2.3 bushels of oats
and 2 bushels of barley were planted.

In Iowa and Ohio, 8 or 9 hours of man labor and 13 or
14 hours of horse work were used per acre of oats; in New
York, 16 hours of man labor and 16.8 hours of horse work
were used on the farms studied.

On all of these farms the oats were planted by broad-
casting. The soil was prepared by discing and was not

plowed. Drilling the seed, in Ohio, added one-half hour of labor per acre. Most of the threshing on these farms was from the shock.

Variations in harvesting methods and labor used. Table XVIII (page 155) shows the variations in amount of labor required to harvest and thresh an acre of small grain by three different methods. Storing the grain in

Courtesy J. I. Case

Fig. 24.—Mechanical corn pickers reduce the fall labor peak.

the barn and then threshing it took about an hour per acre longer than threshing from the shock. Threshing from the barn is used to avoid loss in localities where heavy rains are liable to occur during the harvest season.

Seasonal distribution of labor for oats and barley. In the corn belt states, the first labor peak for oats and barley occurs from the last of March to the latter part of April when the seedbed is being prepared and the crop planted. The land is usually disced and not plowed, and the seed is broadcast from an endgate seeder. The second labor peak occurs from the middle of July until late July and early August when the crop is harvested and threshed. These labor requirements are shown in Fig. 25. While the oat crop produces less feed and is less valuable than corn, it takes less labor and uses the labor at times when corn requires little or no attention.

TABLE XVII

SUMMARY OF REQUIREMENTS PER ACRE IN RAISING OATS

REQUIREMENTS	IOWA[a] 1927	OHIO 1920-1924	NEW YORK[c] 1920-1927
Acres of Oats per Farm.......	28	13	13
Yield, bushels per acre........	44	32	41
Labor and Materials Used:			
Seed, bushels.............	3.7	2.7	2.3
Fertilizer, pounds.........	0	....	154
Twine, pounds.............	2.6	2.3	....
Man labor, hours..........	9.0	8.3	16.0
Horse work, hours.........	13.1	13.7	16.8
Tractor use, hours.........	.5	....	2.3

[a] From Iowa Bulletin 261.
[b] From Ohio Bulletin 396.
[c] From mimeographed publication: "Results of Cost Accounts on Grain Crops," by J. F. Harriott and L. M. Vaughan, Cornell University, 1931.

Place of oats or barley in the farm organization. The complementary relationship between oats and corn, as far as labor is concerned, and the function of oats as a nurse crop for new seedings of hay, make oats worth while in a rotation where the crop would not, in many cases, be justified by its market value. The oat crop has an advantage in the dairy section, because it has a higher percentage of protein than corn or barley.

Barley requires practically the same labor as oats, and also serves as a nurse crop. The relative yields of the two crops under local soil and climatic conditions should

Table XVIII

METHODS OF HARVESTING SMALL GRAINS—ACRES AND YIELDS BY METHODS, AND TIME CONSUMED PER ACRE, 1930-1931[a]

METHOD OF HARVESTING	AREA HARVESTED	AVERAGE YIELD	TIME PER ACRE— ALL HARVESTING OPERATIONS		
	Acres	Bushels	Man Hours	Horse Hours	Tractor Hours
Wheat, total..............	3,511	30.8	7.23	5.64	.23
Threshed from shock.....	3,025	30.5	8.26	5.86	0
Threshed from barn......	145	32.6	1.75	.81	.52
Combine harvester.......	341				
Barley, total..............	2,088	31.2	6.52	5.19	.26
Threshed from shock.....	1,870	27.3	7.00	5.47	0
Threshed from barn......	73	35.9	1.61	.78	.53
Combine harvester.......	145				
Oats, total..............	5,516	43.1	6.39	5.19	.23
Threshed from shock.....	5,150	43.3	7.66	5.00	.12
Threshed from barn......	222	44.9	1.75	.66	.56
Combine harvester.......	144				

[a] From Michigan Special Bulletin 241.

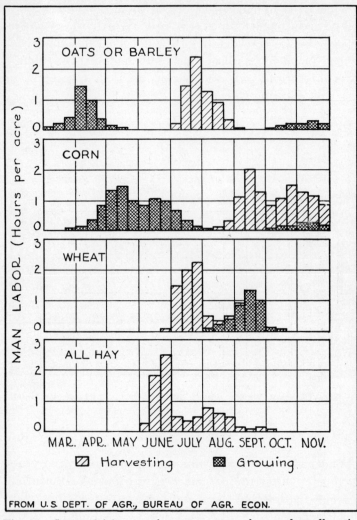

Fig. 25.—Seasonal labor requirement on corn, hay, and small grain.

be considered in choosing between them.   Whether they will be used for fattening meat animals or for dairy cattle should also be considered.   In some localities the yield of feed per acre has been decidedly increased by planting a mixture of oats and barley, or a mixture of oats, barley, and spring wheat.

Photo J. C. Allen and Son

Fig. 26.—Planting winter wheat after corn complicates the labor program.

Winter Wheat

Wheat also serves as a nurse crop for clover and grass seedings. Otherwise, its place in the farm organization is decidedly different; oats and barley are feed crops, but wheat is raised for sale.   Even when raised on diversified farms, wheat is often an important source of cash income.

The seasonal labor requirements of winter wheat are different from those of oats or barley.   The seedbed must be prepared and the crop planted in the fall.   The land may be plowed in the slack season of August or September, or it may be disced after the corn is removed for silage or cut and shocked for grain.   Discing the seedbed after the corn is husked saves labor but rushes the work of removing the corn.

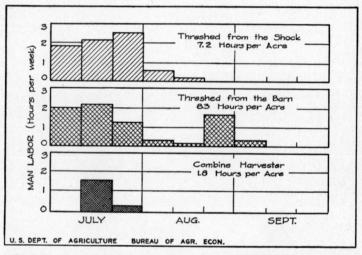

Fig. 27.—Labor used in harvesting wheat by different methods.

Threshing wheat requires about the same amount of labor and power as threshing oats or barley; however, wheat is harvested a week or two earlier.   For this reason there is between wheat and corn greater competition for labor (see Fig. 25), and hence strong reason for not raising it instead of oats in the corn belt.

Labor and material requirements.   Table XIX gives a summary of the average amounts of labor and materials used in raising wheat on farms studied in Iowa, Ohio, and New York.   The amount of seed averaged about 7 pecks per acre in Iowa, and between 8 and 9 pecks in

New York. Twine amounted to 3.1 pounds per acre in Iowa, and 2.4 in Ohio.

In preparing the land and seeding the wheat, the Iowa farms used an average of 3.3 hours of labor and 9.7 hours of horse work. In harvesting, they used 8.4 hours of labor and 8.5 hours of horse work. The farms from which the figures for the various crops were obtained appeared

TABLE XIX

SUMMARY OF REQUIREMENTS PER ACRE IN
RAISING WINTER WHEAT

REQUIREMENTS	Iowa[a] 1925-1927	Ohio[b] 1921-1924	New York[c] 1927-1930
Acres of Wheat per Farm	18.1	27.4	18.9
Yield per Acre, bushels	22.6	19.8	21.4
Labor and Materials Used:			
Seed, bushels	1.8	1.9	2.1
Fertilizer, pounds	..	..	197
Twine, pounds	3.1	2.4	..
Man labor, hours:			
Fall seeding	3.3⎫	8.3	⎧ 7.4
Harvesting and threshing	8.4⎭		⎩ 7.2
Horse work, hours:			
Fall seeding	9.7⎫	12.0	⎧10.3
Harvesting and threshing	8.5⎭		⎩ 4.4
Tractor work, hours	.7	..	3.0

[a] From Iowa Bulletin 261.
[b] From Ohio Bulletin 396.
[c] From mimeographed publication: "Results of Cost Accounts on Grain Crops," by J. F. Harriott and L. M. Vaughan, Cornell University, 1931.

to be rather above the average of the community. However, the most efficient farmers raised their crops with considerably less labor. Figures one fourth lower might be a good standard to strive for.

Clover and Timothy Hay

A mixture of red clover and timothy is the most common hay crop in the corn belt and in the northeastern part of the United States. Clover has a higher protein content than timothy and is, therefore, a more desirable feed, especially if used with corn or other low-protein feeds. It is more difficult, however, to obtain a good stand of clover than of timothy, and the clover is liable to die out after the first year. Moreover, timothy can be raised under some climatic and soil conditions where clover cannot be. The two are commonly mixed as a means of insuring a crop.

Place of hay in the cropping system. How much hay should be included in the cropping system? The acreage depends largely on the number of roughage-consuming livestock. That, in turn, depends partly on the acreage of permanent pasture and partly on relative prices. If grain which may be sold for cash is relatively high priced, the tendency will be toward larger acreage of grain and less of hay. If, on the other hand, cattle or sheep prices are high, the proportion of hay crops will be increased in order to produce more cattle, sheep, or dairy products. Each farmer must work out the proper proportions of hay and grain crops for his own farm.

Labor requirements in harvesting hay. Some data on amounts of labor commonly used in harvesting and storing clover and timothy hay are shown in Table XX. The amount of labor used depends on the yield per acre, the type of equipment, the efficiency of the workers, and other factors such as the distance from the field to the barn, and so on.

In Iowa an average of 5.7 hours of labor was used in harvesting and putting up hay which yielded 1.2 tons per acre. In New York the average was 8 hours of labor and 8.8 hours of horse work for hay yielding 1.6 tons per acre.

The harvest time for hay is short. In the Iowa study,

haying was done from the last week of June to the third
week in July.   The harvest should be finished in a period
of time shorter than this so that the quality of the hay
will not deteriorate.   In Iowa the early part of hay harvest conflicts with the last cultivation of corn, and the
latter part with the wheat or oat harvest.

TABLE XX

LABOR USED IN HARVESTING CLOVER AND TIMOTHY HAY

REQUIREMENTS	IOWA[a] 1925-1927	OHIO[b] 1920-1924	NEW YORK[c] 1927-1930
Acres of Hay per Farm.......	16.1	14.7	33.7
Yield per Acre, tons..........	1.2	1.1	1.6
Labor Used in Harvesting, per acre:			
Labor, hours.............	5.7	7.3	8.0
Horse work, hours.........	8.4	8.5	8.8
Labor Used in Harvesting, per ton:			
Labor, hours.............	4.7	6.6	5.0
Horse work, hours.........	7.0	7.7	5.5

[a] From Iowa Bulletin 261.
[b] From Ohio Bulletin 396.
[c] From mimeographed publication: "Results of Cost Accounts on Hay and Corn Silage,"
by J. F. Harriott and L. M. Vaughan, Cornell University, 1931.

Alfalfa

Where alfalfa can be grown, its high yield and high
protein content make it easily the best of the hay crops.
Difficulties in raising alfalfa arise from the fact that it
cannot tolerate an acid or a wet soil.   Once alfalfa is
established, it is profitable to leave the crop until it begins
to die out, rather than use it in the customary short rotation.

Labor Requirements.   Twelve to fifteen hours per
acre can usually be counted on as the labor needed to
harvest the three cuttings of alfalfa.   The first cutting

is heaviest and occurs about the middle of June. In the corn belt, the second cutting is done about the last of July and the third the middle of September.

Table XXI, based on figures from Michigan, shows the variation in amount of labor needed for the different cuttings in the southeastern part of that state. The first required 5.5 hours per acre, the second 3.8 hours, and the third 3.3. However, the labor requirements, ex-

TABLE XXI

HARVESTING ALFALFA HAY
(From Michigan Special Bulletin 241)

			TIME CONSUMED IN MAKING HAY		
			PER ACRE		PER TON
	ACREAGE STUDIED	AVERAGE YIELD	Man Hours	Horse Hours	Man Hours
	Number	Tons			
First Cutting......	1,983	1.46	5.5	7.3	3.8
Second Cutting....	1,618	.64	3.8	5.4	6.0
Third Cutting.....	159	.38	3.3	4.5	8.8

pressed per ton of hay, were quite different, because of the heavier yield of the first cutting. The labor amounted to 3.8 hours per ton on the first cutting, 6.0 hours on the second, and 8.8 hours on the third.

Soybeans

Soybeans are a very versatile crop. The beans can be used as a protein supplement in feeding and the hay is also rich in protein. Soybeans cannot compete with alfalfa where that crop can be grown, but they will grow on an acid soil. They are useful also as an emergency crop after clover or alfalfa fails to make a stand. The methods of raising the crop depend on its purpose in the farm organization.

Place of soybeans in the farm organization.   The best time for planting soybeans is about corn planting time. If they are planted in rows and cultivated, they also compete with corn cultivation.

If raised for hay, soybeans lighten the labor load during June and July, since they are harvested during the September slack period.   If the crop is harvested for seed, labor is required during August or September, and this arrangement also helps even out the seasonal labor requirements.

Soybeans may be used to replace part of the oat or other small grain crop.   In some sections they may be used instead of corn for part of the rotation, or they may replace other hay crops.   They may be followed in the rotation either by corn or a small grain crop.   The land will need very little preparation if a small grain is to be planted.   Wheat may be seeded at the same time that the beans are harvested; this can be done by having a drill driven immediately behind the binder so that the bundles of beans fall on land which has already been seeded.

Soybeans, by loosening up the soil, help in preparing for the next crop, but this also causes erosion on rolling land. Either the beans should not be planted on soil that is likely to erode easily, or they should be followed by a crop, such as winter wheat, which will hold the soil in the fall after the beans are removed.

Labor requirements for soybeans.   Tables XXII to XXIV show the amounts of labor used in raising and harvesting soybeans in 202 fields in Iowa in 1931 and 1932.   The beans may be drilled or broadcast, or they may be planted in rows with a corn planter or with a grain drill with part of its spouts stopped up.   If planted in rows, the crop is usually cultivated.   If the beans are to be drilled solid, the ground should be plowed in the fall or early spring, and then left for at least two weeks to allow the weeds to start.   These are killed by discing again just before the beans are planted.

Table XXII shows that drilling the crop in solid appears to be the most economical method.   It required

TABLE XXII

LABOR AND POWER USED IN GROWING SOYBEANS
UP TO HARVEST

(From Iowa Bulletin 309)

METHOD OF PLANTING	No. OF FIELDS	HOURS PER ACRE		
		Man	Horse	Tractor
Broadcast.................	9	3.7	12.1	.5
Drilled solid..............	115	4.1	9.8	.5
Planted with corn planter....	50	6.8	17.1	.8
Drilled in 21″ to 28″ rows....	28	4.7	7.6	1.9
Average..............	202	4.8	11.5	.8

TABLE XXIII

LABOR AND POWER USED IN HARVESTING SOYBEANS
FOR SEED

(From Iowa Bulletin 309)

METHOD USED	HOURS PER ACRE		
	Man	Horse	Tractor
Bind, shock, thresh..........	6.8	8.3	.8
Mow, rake, thresh...........	9.3	10.2	.9
Combine...................	2.4	2.2	.8
Average[a]..............	6.5	7.8	.8

[a] Based on records from 101 fields, average yield 22.1 bushels per acre.

about 4 hours of man labor and 10 hours of horse work before harvesting.

There are three common methods of harvesting the beans for seed. They may be cut with a binder, shocked, and later threshed. They may be cut with a mower, and then raked, hauled, and threshed loose. In Iowa this method required more labor than the use of the binder and caused more loss of seed by shattering. The com-

TABLE XXIV

LABOR AND POWER USED TO PUT UP SOYBEAN HAY

(From Iowa Bulletin 309)

METHOD USED	No. OF FIELDS	HOURS PER ACRE		
		Man	Horse	Tractor
Mow, rake, cock by hand, unload power	27	13.0	11.2	..
Mow, rake, cock by rake, load by hand, unload power	18	9.5	11.4	..
Mow, cure in swath or windrow, hay loader, unload power	21	7.0	9.9	.2
Cut binder, shock, load by hand, unload with slings	24	9.2	11.4	.2
Average of all methods[a]		10.1	10.8	.1

[a] Average yield 2.2 tons per acre.

binc, however, proves the most economical of man labor and horse work, but the straw cannot be saved readily. Labor and power requirements in harvesting for grain are shown in Table XXIII.

Harvesting soybeans for hay. The amounts of labor and power used in harvesting soybeans for hay are shown in Table XXIV. The hay may be raked, and then cocked by hand and loaded by hand. A second method is to cock the hay with the rake and to load by hand.

The hay loader is the most economical method, since it saves about 2½ hours of labor per ton; however, too many leaves may be lost if the hay is allowed to become too dry in the field. An apron should be used on the loader to save leaves and beans. A fourth method is to harvest the hay with a binder and leave it in the shock for ten days or longer. This method produces a good quality of hay with little shattering. If labor is available and is not too expensive, the hay loader should not be used, because it usually results in a poorer quality of hay and considerable shattering.

Thick planting of soybeans is recommended. If they are planted in 42-inch rows, about one bushel of beans is required per acre. For 21-inch rows it takes about 1.8 bushels; if the beans are drilled solid two bushels give the maximum yield of seed. Thick planting also improves the quality of the hay, since the stems are finer and the hay is relatively free from weeds.

Potatoes

Approximate standard requirements for the production of potatoes are difficult to give because the crop is raised under such a wide range of climatic conditions. Dates of planting, harvesting, and other operations depend largely on the climate, the variety of potatoes and the market for which they are being grown. These in turn affect the relationships between potatoes and other crops.

Crop-raising methods differ widely from one area to another, even in the same state. As an illustration, 40 out of 41 farmers from whom records were obtained in northern New York in 1929 used two-horse teams in plowing. They spent, on an average, 15.4 hours of labor

TABLE XXV

LABOR AND MATERIALS USED PER ACRE IN GROWING
POTATOES IN NORTHERN STATES

REQUIREMENTS	Western New York[a] 1929	Northern New York[a] 1929	Long Island[a] 1929	Michigan Montcalm County[b] 1919	Maine Aroostook County[b] 1919
Acres per farm.........	12.4	7.8	56.2	10.0	28.0
Yield per acre, bushels...	153	217	149	109	278
Seed, bushels...........	18.0	14.8	16.9	7.7	15.4
Fertilizer, pounds.......	416	763	2,158	421[e]	1,980[e]
Manure, tons..........	6.0	9.5	.3	12.9[e]	10.4[e]
Labor, hours:					
Plowing and fitting....	6.8	15.4	2.4	..	..
Preparing seed........	11.2	9.8	8.3	..	..
Fertilizing and planting	5.5	9.9	4.8	..	..
Cultivating and tilling.	12.3	19.1	11.5	..	..
Spraying and dusting..	2.3	5.8	4.6	..	..
Total growing......	38.1	60.0	31.6	..	..
Digging..............	4.2	..[d]	4.2	..	..
Picking up...........	21.5	..[d]	14.9	..	..
Total harvesting[c]....	25.8	57.2	19.2	..	..
Grading..............	9.7	..[d]	..[d]	..	..
Selling..............	2.7	..[d]	..[d]	..	..
Total..............	12.4				
Total labor, hours[e].	81.5	145.2	58.4	73.9	77.6[f]
Horse work, hours:					
Growing.............	47.0	72.3	34.4	..	..
Harvesting..........	13.5	7.3	9.6	..	..
Selling..............	.7	..[d]	..[d]	..	..
Total horse work, hours...........	01.2	70.6	46 1[c]	85.5	110.0
Tractor work, hours.....	3.5	.6	3.2	..	..

[a] From Cornell Bulletin 568.
[b] From U.S. Department of Agriculture, Department Bulletin 1188.
[c] Contains items not listed separately.
[d] Not given.
[e] Total on acres covered.
[f] Picking time not included, largely contract.

in preparing the seedbed. In the Long Island area of the same state, 84 percent of the growers plowed with a tractor, using 2.4 hours in preparing the seedbed.

Total labor in growing the crop amounted to 31.6 hours per acre in the Long Island area, as compared with 60 hours in northern New York. In harvesting, Long Island used 19.2 hours, as compared with 57.2 hours in northern New York.

In comparing, from Table XXV, the total number of hours used in raising and harvesting the crop in different areas and years, we find, surprisingly, that some areas in 1929 were using more labor per acre than others had used in 1919, although a great deal of labor-saving equipment had been developed in the intervening ten years.

While growing costs may be reduced by the use of large-capacity equipment, its economical use requires a large acreage. The cost per bushel may also be lowered by raising the yield per acre, unless the additional yield requires too much expensive fertilizer. Specific plans for raising this crop should be worked out with the aid of the county agent and the agricultural experiment station.

References

Hughes, H. D., and Henson, E. R., *Crop Production*, Macmillan, New York, 1930.

Illinois Agricultural Experiment Station, Department of Agricultural Economics, mimeographed publication: "A Guide to Farm Planning," by R. R. Hudelson.

Iowa Bulletin 261: "The Crop System in Iowa County," by J. A. Hopkins, 1929.

Iowa Bulletin 289: "Costs and Utilization of Corn in Seven Iowa Counties," by H. L. Thomas and John A. Hopkins, 1932.

Iowa Bulletin 309: "Soybeans in Iowa Farming," by Albert Mighell, H. D. Hughes, and F. S. Wilkins, 1934.

Iowa Bulletin 331: "Choosing Legumes and Perennial Grasses," by F. S. Wilkins and H. D. Hughes, 1935.

Kentucky Bulletin 274: "Man Labor, Horse Work and Materials Used in Producing Crops in Christian County," by J. B. Hutson and W. G. Finn, 1926.

Michigan Special Bulletin 241: "A Farm Management Study of Crop Production Practices," by P. G. Minneman and E. B. Hill, 1933.

Mississippi Bulletin 256: "Progress Report on Cost of Production Route in Jones County, Mississippi, 1927," by Lewis E. Long and J. R. Allen, 1928.

New York, Cornell Bulletin 568: "Costs and Returns in Producing Potatoes in New York in 1929," by F. L. Underwood, 1932.

New York, Cornell, mimeographed publication: "Results of Cost Accounts on Grain Crops," by J. F. Harriott and L. M. Vaughan, 1931.

New York, Cornell, mimeographed publication: "Results of Cost Accounts on Hay and Corn Silage," by J. F. Harriott and L. M. Vaughan, 1931.

Ohio Bulletin 396: "Variations in Costs of Producing Corn, Wheat and Other Crops in Greene County, Ohio," by J. I. Falconer and J. F. Dowler, 1926.

Pennsylvania Bulletin 292: "Labor Requirements for Pennsylvania Farms," by J. E. McCord and C. E. Cronemeyer, 1933.

Purdue Bulletin 306: "Costs and Profits in Producing Soybeans in Indiana," by C. E. Young and L. G. Hobson, 1926.

South Dakota Circular 4: "A Handbook on South Dakota Farm Production Costs," by M. R. Benedict, 1923.

U.S. Department of Agriculture, Department Bulletin 1188: "Costs and Farm Practices in Producing Potatoes," by W. C. Funk, 1924.

U.S. Department of Agriculture, Department Bulletin 1292: "Field and Crop Labor on Georgia Farms," by L. A. Reynoldson, 1925.

U.S. Department of Agriculture, Technical Bulletin 244: "Harvesting Small Grains, Soybeans and Clover in the Corn Belt with Combines and Binders," by L. A. Reynoldson, W. R. Humphries, and J. H. Martin, 1931.

U.S. Department of Agriculture, Yearbook, 1924: article on "Hay," by Piper and others.

Part IV

THE LIVESTOCK SYSTEM

CHAPTER XII

Purposes of Livestock in the Farm Organization

The Problem: Why should farmers keep livestock? Is it possible to maintain the soil fertility without livestock enterprises? Would it be as profitable, in most regions, to farm without livestock? What parts do livestock enterprises play in the farm organization?

Livestock and Conservation of Fertility

Helping to maintain the fertility of the soil is one of the more important purposes of livestock enterprises. Of course, soil productivity can be kept up by the use of green manure crops and commercial fertilizers, but these methods have generally been less popular than the use of livestock. This is partly because the use of green manure crops as the only source of organic matter means keeping part of the land each year in crops which yield no direct returns.

If cattle or sheep are kept, it is possible to pasture these soil-building crops part of the time. This yields a direct return and at the same time leaves part of the crop to turn under. On most farms the use of manure and green manure is sufficient to keep up the productivity of the soil.

On farms where large amounts of feed are bought for steers or dairy cattle, it is even possible to increase soil productivity in a few years. Manure usually improves the texture of soil, but it must be used intelligently and not wasted.

If mineral elements, such as lime, phosphorus, or potash, are seriously deficient, it will be necessary to apply these in addition to the manures. A soil management program, however, need not attempt to replace all plant food removed from the soil. The question of whether or not to buy a mineral fertilizer will usually be settled

Fig. 28.—A small flock of sheep converts low-grade roughage into a marketable product.

by the cost of the fertilizer and the value of the increase in yield.

Livestock may convert crops into more valuable products. Livestock enterprises also serve to convert some products into more valuable things. While cattle and sheep can use low-grade or unsalable roughage to produce beef or mutton, they cannot live on these things alone. They must also have some higher-grade feeds. Other elements of production besides feed must be used as well. Labor and shelter are required in increasing amounts as the fattening process advances.

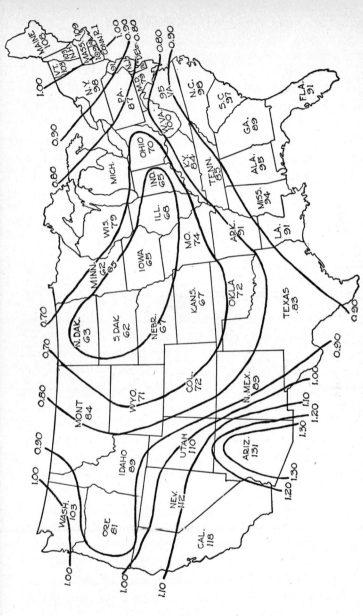

Fig. 29.—Average price of corn received by producers, December 1 price in cents per bushel, five-year average (1925-1929).

Low-grade grains, such as soft corn, may be fed to hogs. Roughages not worth hauling or shipping may be fed to cattle or sheep. Horses, and cattle which are not being milked or fattened for market get much of their winter feed from straw stacks and corn stalks.

How can we tell whether or not it will be profitable to feed the necessary grain to livestock in order to supplement these unsalable products? *As long as the livestock promise to return more than the value of marketable feeds plus actual cash outlay, the farmer will be better off if he utilizes unsalable feeds, labor in slack seasons, and buildings or equipment which would otherwise remain idle.*

Transportation Expenses Affect Disposition of Crops

The expense of getting some products to market is an important influence on the choice and size of livestock enterprises. The cost of shipping bulky crop materials long distances to market often dictates that they be changed into products of smaller bulk and greater value per pound before they are marketed. This was pointed out in Chapter II as one of the influences determining the location of types of farming areas. Thus, roughages and grains in the corn belt are commonly converted into beef or pork before they are marketed. Just why is this necessary?

If we examine a few freight rates we will see why large amounts of corn are fed to hogs or steers in the Middle West, while the eastern farmer is at a disadvantage in the production of meat animals. Let us suppose that a central Iowa farmer uses 500 pounds of grain in producing 100 pounds of gain on hogs. If he is fattening steers, he uses about 850 pounds of grain plus 350 pounds of roughage for each 100 pounds of gain produced.

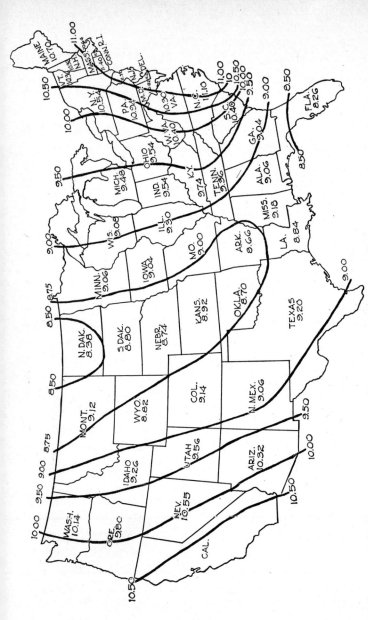

Fig. 30.—Average price of hogs received by producers, December 1 price, five-year average (1925-1929).

177

Freight Rates from Central Iowa to Chicago, per 100 pounds		*Freight Rates from Chicago to New York, per 100 pounds*	
Corn	$.185	Corn	$.30[a]
Hogs	.39	Hogs	.51[a]
Cattle	.34	Cattle	.51[a]
Hay	.21	Hay	.87
		Dressed meat	.53

[a] Proportional rate on shipments originating west of Chicago.

From these freight rates we see that if a farmer were to ship a carload of corn from central Iowa to New York, the combined freight rate would be 48.5 cents per hundred pounds. This would amount to $2.425 on the 500 pounds that would be required to produce the 100 pounds of hogs. The freight on 100 pounds of hogs is 90 cents, a saving of $1.535 which gives the Iowa farmer an important advantage over the eastern farmer in hog production.

On cattle the saving is even greater, since the freight on 850 pounds of corn would be $4.12 and on 350 pounds of hay $2.59. If the cattle were slaughtered in Chicago and the meat shipped east, the freight on them would be still less, since cattle dress only a little over half the live weight.

Livestock and the Utilization of Rough Land

A farm often has land too rough to cultivate to advantage, or a field that is low-lying and subject to frequent overflow. Such land is usually pastured. On rough upland either cattle or sheep may be used but on low, wet land there is apt to be difficulty with sheep on account of parasites or footrot.

If such land is fertile and not extremely rough, the farmer may alternate between pasture and crops in periods of several years. As the grass becomes thin, it may be plowed up and put into crops. After the rotation comes around to seeding it down, it may be left in grass again for several more years. In this way it is often possible to keep such land either in a productive pasture or in still more valuable crops.

If there is much rough land, the whole farming system must be planned to make use of it, even though the rest of the land may be level and very productive.   Cattle or

Fig. 31.—Beef cattle utilize rough land.

sheep will be kept to make use of the pasture.   Since they need roughage in winter as well as summer, sufficient hay must be included in the cropping system, as well as the necessary grain.   If enough livestock is kept to make use of much rough land, there will be considerable manure to keep up the fertility of the farm.   This helps explain why rough farms often maintain their fertility over a long period of years better than smooth farms which have been used chiefly to produce cash grain crops.

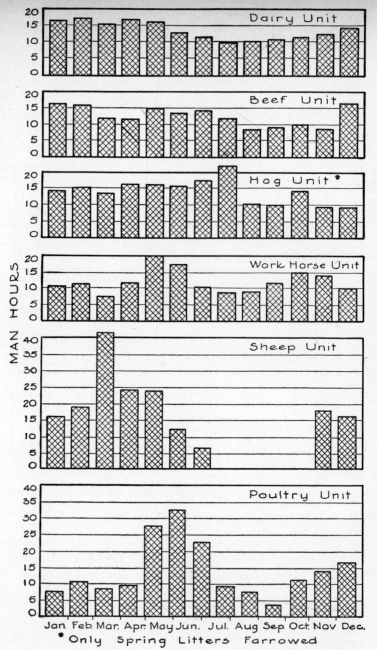

Fig. 32.—Distribution of labor by four-week periods on composite units of various classes of livestock. Data from Minnesota Bulletin 283.

Dairy unit equals 1 cow, .25 heifer, and .07 bull.
Beef unit equals 4.5 cows, 3.33 baby beeves, .67 heifer, .67 calf, and .14 bull.
Hog unit (only spring litters farrowed) equals 5 sows and litters.
Work horse unit equals 2 horses.
Sheep unit equals 60 ewes.
Poultry unit equals 50 hens and 100 chicks.

Livestock and the Utilization of Labor

One reason for keeping livestock is that they utilize labor in the winter and other slack seasons. This is not equally true for all types of livestock. Nor are the seasonal labor requirements identical for the same live-stock project in different localities. Fig. 32 shows that

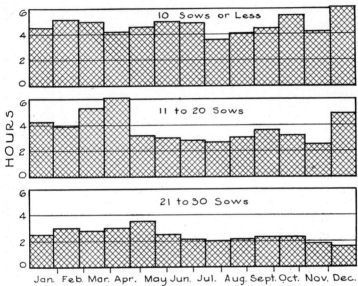

Fig. 33.—Labor used per sow—Iowa county, Iowa—Comparison by size of hog enterprise. Hours per sow per period of four weeks.

in the Red River Valley of Minnesota hogs required the most labor during June and July. These farms usually kept from 3 to 7 sows per farm, and the pigs were farrowed in April, May, and June. Fig. 33 shows that in eastern Iowa little labor is required for hogs in June and July, since most of the pigs are farrowed in March and April. The climate is mostly responsible for the difference be-tween the two areas.

The total amount of labor required by the livestock on any farm depends, of course, on which enterprises are kept and on their size. On diversified Iowa farms about 50 hours per week were required by livestock in March and April. In the latter part of the summer about 30 hours and from December through February about 40 hours, were spent.

On the diversified farm it is by no means true that the farmer has all his time free for crop work in the spring and summer, nor is his time fully used by livestock during the winter. Nevertheless, the livestock projects do help in smoothing out the peaks and valleys in the year's labor calendar.

Labor on hogs. Fig. 33 shows the labor required per sow and litter for small groups of farms in Iowa County, Iowa. On these farms there were between one-third and one-half as many fall as spring litters. The farms with the largest numbers of sows were usually those raising only spring litters. Fig. 33 shows that the labor per sow was less where the hog enterprise was large.

There is also a difference in labor requirements as between spring and fall pigs. In the Iowa County study there were about 20 records on farms which had only spring pigs, and an equal number with both spring and fall litters. The total amount of labor per 100 pounds of gain was almost the same in each case, averaging 2.7 and 2.6 hours respectively. There was a saving of labor on the breeding herd on the two litter farms, but the fall pigs needed more attention after weaning than the spring pigs. There was more difference in the distribution of labor than in the total amount. Where there were two litters the spring pigs were usually farrowed somewhat earlier and there were two peak labor seasons, one in March and April and the second from late August into

October.   With only spring litters, the spring labor peak
was less pronounced.

Labor on cattle.   Beef cattle require less labor per
head than dairy cows, and there is also less seasonal
variation.   In Fig. 32 is shown the labor distribution on
the Red River Valley farms on groups of livestock which

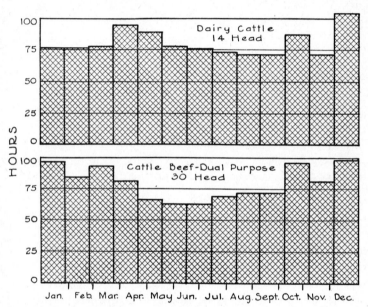

Fig. 34.—Seasonal distribution of labor on cattle.   Hours per period
of four weeks, Iowa county, Iowa.

required about the same amount of work during the year.
Dairy cattle required the most labor during the winter
and spring and the least during the summer.   Beef cattle
required the most during the winter, late spring, and
early summer.

Figure 34 shows that 14 head of dairy cattle, including
other stock as well as cows, required the same amount of
work as 30 head of beef or dual purpose cattle.

Diminishing returns from labor used on livestock. The principle of diminishing economic returns operates in the application of labor to livestock as well as to other phases of the farm business. Using the hog project as an example, too little attention at farrowing time may result in large losses of pigs. A little more time spent at this period may bring more than a proportionate increase in production and subsequent returns. But after this seriously needed attention has been given, more labor may bring only small increase, and later, no further increase at all in the returns.

The amount of labor used on an entire enterprise per unit of production is often taken as a measure of one's efficiency. Actually, the amount of time used on each operation is a better measure. More work with pigs after they are weaned would not offset losses due to neglect at farrowing time. This same thing is just as true with the other livestock projects.

Since a farmer has only a limited amount of labor, his problem is how to distribute it best among his different enterprises. If he spends too much time with poultry, he will not have enough time left to give his dairy or hogs the proper care. Of course, the most advantageous distribution of labor will vary from week to week. The farmer should try to distribute it so that the last few hours spent per week on one project will not keep him from some other job that might bring a greater return.

References

Henry, W. A., and Morrison, F. B., *Feeds and Feeding* (18th edition), Henry-Morrison Co., Madison, Wisc., 1923, Chapter VIII.

Overton, M. H., and Robertson, L. S., *Profitable Farm Management*, Lippincott, Philadelphia, 1929, Chapter VII.

Warren, G. F., *Farm Management*, Macmillan, New York, 1916, Chapters V and VI.

Illinois Bulletin 261: "Cattle Feeding in Relation to Farm Management," by H. C. M. Case and K. H. Myers, 1925.

Illinois Bulletin 301: "The Place of Hog Production in Corn-Belt Farming," by H. C. M. Case and R. C. Ross, 1927.

Illinois Bulletin 390: "Some Important Factors Affecting Costs in Hog Production," by R. H. Wilcox, W. E. Carroll, and T. G. Hornung, 1933.

Iowa Bulletin 242: "An Economic Study of the Cattle Feeding Enterprise in Iowa," by J. A. Hopkins, 1927.

Iowa Bulletin 270: "The Livestock System in Iowa County," by J. A. Hopkins and R. S. Kifer, 1930.

Iowa Bulletin 294: "An Economic Study of the Hog Enterprise," by J. A. Hopkins, 1932.

Minnesota Bulletin 270: "Factors Affecting the Physical and Economic Cost of Butterfat Production in Pine County, Minnesota," by George A. Pond and Mordecai Ezekiel, 1930.

Minnesota Bulletin 283: "An Economic Study of Livestock Possibilities in the Red River Valley of Minnesota," by George A. Sallee, George A. Pond, and C. W. Crickman, 1931.

New Jersey Bulletin 534: "Farm Profits and Factors Influencing Farm Profits on 176 Farms in Hunterdon County," by Allen G. Waller and Emil Rauchenstine, 1932.

New York State College of Agriculture (Cornell), Mimeographed publication: "Results of Cost Accounts on Livestock," by J. F. Harriott and L. M. Vaughan, 1931.

Oregon Station Circular 94: "Cost of Producing Sheep on Western Oregon Farms," by Oran M. Nelson, 1929.

U.S. Department of Agriculture, Technical Bulletin 23: "Costs and Methods of Fattening Beef Cattle in the Corn Belt, 1919-23," by R. H. Wilcox, R. D. Jennings, G. W. Collier, W. H. Black, and E. W. McComas, 1927.

U.S. Department of Agriculture, Department Bulletin 1454: "Factors in the Cost of Producing Beef in the Flint Hills Section of Kansas," by R. H. Wilcox, W. E. Grimes, Morris Evans and H. J. Henney, 1926.

CHAPTER XIII

The Feed Supply and the Livestock System

The Problem: What are the feed requirements of various kinds of livestock? How much can the combination of feeds for any one kind of stock be varied? How do the available feed supply and the needs of the various types of livestock determine the livestock enprises of the farm?

Feed Crops Determine the Livestock Projects

The kind and amount of available feed crops are most important in deciding which livestock to keep. If the crop system produces much feed grain and only a little roughage, hogs will probably be the most important livestock project. If there is much roughage and little grain, sheep or cattle will fit into the organization better. If we put prices on the materials and services used in producing livestock, we find that most of the total cost is for feed. The figures in Table XXVI show this very forcibly.

When feed is relatively cheap and plentiful, livestock enterprises tend to be large, and a large part of the outlay is for feed. This may simply mean that there is a saving of labor in having a large-sized project. But there is also a tendency on the part of the farmer to use more of the factor of production (feed in this case) that is cheapest.

In New York, feeds are relatively higher-priced than,

Table XXVI

FEED AND TOTAL EXPENSES

| | ILLINOIS[a] | IOWA Iowa Co. | MINNESOTA | | NEW YORK[c] |
| | | | Rock and Nobles Cos.[b] | Pine County | |
	1930	1925-1927	1930	1925-1927	1927-1930
Hogs, per cwt. gain:					
Total Expense...	$8.04	$9.98	$6.49	$11.47	$20.39[d]
Value of feed....	$6.16	$7.39	$5.18	$8.44	$12.04
Per cent for feed.	75	74	80	74	59
Dairy Cows, per head per year:					
Total Expense...	$143.00	....	....	$131.00	$227.00
Value of feed....	$94.00	....	....	$72.00	$114.00
Per cent for feed.	66	....	....	55	50
Beef and Dual Purpose Cattle, per animal unit per year:					
Total Expense...	....	$75.00	$11.05[e]	....	....
Value of feed....	....	$44.00	$9.67	....	....
Per cent for feed.	....	59	87	....	....
Feeding Steers, per cwt. gain:					
Total Expense...	....	$18.31	$14.89	....	....
Value of feed....	....	$13.86	$12.81	....	....
Per cent for feed.	....	76	87	....	....
Horses, per head per year:					
Total Expense...	$111.00	$96.00	$79.00	$97.00	$157.00
Value of feed....	$72.00	$60.00	$47.00	$51.00	$79.00
Per cent for feed.	65	63	60	53	50

[a] Nineteen farms in Champaign and Piatt Counties, by courtesy of Prof. R. H. Wilcox, University of Illinois.
[b] By courtesy of Prof. George A. Pond, University of Minnesota.
[c] From various New York counties, by courtesy of Prof. J. F. Harriott, Cornell University.
[d] Per pig fatted or per sow kept.
[e] Per hundred pounds of gain.

for example, in Iowa or Minnesota, while labor is cheaper. The effect on the relative importance of feed in livestock enterprises is shown in Table XXVI. In the Middle West, feed is about 75 percent of the total cost of hog production. In New York, while feeds were decidedly more expensive, they made up only about 60 percent of the total because of the larger outlay for labor, shelter, and so on.

Expenses with dairy cows varied in the same way between the different localities. However, cows require more attention per dollar of product than do hogs, so the labor cost in both cases is a higher percentage of the total.

Steer-feeding is another project which requires much feed in proportion to the amount of labor spent on the animals. In the two cases for which data are available, 76 and 87 per cent, respectively, of the total cost was for feed.

In the keeping of work horses there is also a wide variation in the costs for feed and other purposes. From 50 to 65 per cent was for feed. In New York, the total costs were about twice as high as in southwestern Minnesota and about half again as much as in some other midwestern areas. In the west the horses were allowed to shift for themselves in the winter, much more than were those in New York, where they were fed and cared for in the stables.

In planning the livestock system of a farm, we must know what the feed requirements are for the different kinds of livestock. Let us study these requirements before planning the livestock budget.

Feed Requirements of Hogs

Table XXVII shows the amounts of feed used per hundred pounds of gain on hogs, including the entire hog enterprise.   These figures come from six different studies in three midwestern states.   The total amount of concentrates varied in these studies from 473 to 559 pounds

Photo J. C. Allen and Son

Fig. 35.—The number of hogs raised usually depends upon the supply of corn.

per 100 pounds of gain.   In addition, the hogs consumed various amounts of pasture and minerals.

Except in the Polk County, Minnesota, study, corn was the most important grain fed.   The consumption of corn amounted to about 8 bushels per 100 pounds of

Table XXVII

FEED USED IN PRODUCING 100 LBS. GAIN ON HOGS—ENTIRE HOG ENTERPRISE

| | ILLINOIS[a] | IOWA[b] | | | MINNESOTA | |
	McLean & Woodford Cos.	Humboldt Co.	Webster Co.	Iowa Co.	Jackson & Cottonwood Cos.[c]	Polk Co.[d]
Year of Study	1924-1926	1922-1924	1928-1930	1925-1927	1921	1927
No. Records	106	159	113	59	22	18
Hogs Produced, average pounds per farm	25,407	18,314	17,327	26,761	13,176	10,111
Feeds:						
Corn, pounds	400	457	455	434	432	74
Oats, pounds	39	55	56	38	} 53	} 456
Other Small Grains, pounds	5	} 1	} 22	} 29		
Mill Feeds, pounds	6				4	8
Tankage, pounds	13	5	8	12	4	
Other Protein Feeds, pounds	6	2	5	..	..	} 21
Skim Milk, gallons[e]	5	9	5	4	12	
Total Concentrates, pounds[f]	474	529	551	517	505	559
Pasture, animal unit days[f]	2.1	..	..	..	4.5	12
Minerals, pounds	1.5	..	..	..	..	..
Man labor, hours	1.5	2.0	..	2.4	3.2	4.7
Horse work, hours	.3	..	..	..	.4	.3

[a] Illinois Bulletin 390.
[b] Iowa Bulletin 294.
[c] Minnesota Bulletin 205.
[d] Minnesota Bulletin 283.
[e] In computing total pounds concentrates skim milk is counted at its dry equivalent of .8 lb. per gal.
[f] Pasture, animal unit days, equivalent of pasture consumption by one animal unit. In the Minnesota study the 4.5 animal unit days is given as equivalent of 22.5 for one mature hog or 45 days for one pig under six months.

gain. Besides the corn, one or two bushels of oats were fed. These starchy grains were supplemented by the equivalent of 12 to 20 pounds of tankage. Much of this supplementary feed was skim milk.

The feeds used in Polk County, Minnesota, are particularly interesting when compared with those in the other studies. Here, in the Red River Valley, much more small grain than corn is raised. Consequently the proportion of small grain and corn fed is almost reversed from that in Iowa and Illinois. This shows how one feed can be substituted for another.

The Principle of Substitution

Small grains are substituted for corn in this particular case mostly from necessity. But in many cases substitutions of one feed for another are made on the basis of their relative prices. When the price of barley rises in proportion to that of corn, farmers try to feed more corn and less barley. Often there is a more or less definite limit to such substitution beyond which less satisfactory results are obtained. *The substitution tends to be carried to that point where the technical disadvantage offsets the difference in price.*

This is only one of the many ways in which the principle of substitution is evident. It is one of the most important economic principles. Substitutions may even be made between the basic factors of production, as labor for machinery, or vice versa. It is possible to make substitutions between land and labor and capital. That is, we may raise 100 bushels of corn by using much labor and power, and get high yields from a small amount of land. If land is cheap and labor and capital high, we may use labor and capital more sparingly and get a lower yield per acre from a larger acreage.

Sometimes one raw material is substituted entirely for another. Usually there is no fixed relation between the proportions of the various production factors. Each increase in the use of one factor runs into diminishing returns on that factor and increasing returns on the other. The most profitable place to stop the substitution depends on the relative prices of the factors. We will discuss this important principle later.

Feeds for Different Stages of the Hog Production Process

Hog raising, like most other farm production processes, consists of a series of more or less definite stages. For convenience we may divide the enterprise into the breeding herd and the fattening herd. Rations needed and problems involved are quite different, and figures such as those in Table XXVII are apt to be confusing if carelessly interpreted.

Table XXVIII shows the average consumption of feeds by breeding herds in the Iowa and Illinois studies already referred to. Figures for the two studies cannot be compared directly, because feed requirements in the Illinois study are stated in amounts per sow farrowing, while in the Iowa study they are given as the quantities per animal in the total breeding herd.

Each sow farrowing consumed, in the Illinois study, about 1,550 pounds of corn, slightly over 300 pounds of small grains, and the equivalent of about 100 pounds of tankage in the form of skim milk, tankage, and other feeds. In the Iowa study the corn amounted to 1,378 pounds per hog in the breeding herd, oats 224 pounds, and the equivalent of about 40 pounds of tankage.

Rations in fattening pigs. Table XXIX shows cor-

responding figures for pigs after they are weaned. In
each study about 475 pounds of concentrates were fed
per hundred pounds gained. In the Iowa study more

TABLE XXVIII

FEED USED BY HOGS PER ANIMAL IN BREEDING HERD,
DURING A PRODUCTION YEAR

	ILLINOIS[a]	IOWA[b]
	McLean & Woodford Cos.	Humboldt Co.
Years of Study	1924-1926	1922-1924
No. Records	106	159
No. Sows	17	17
Feeds:		
Corn, pounds	1,549	1,378
Oats, pounds	296	224
Other Small Grains, pounds	31	..
Mill Feeds, pounds	40	4
Tankage, pounds	59	14
Other Protein Feeds, pounds	32	4
Skim Milk, gallons[c]	25	31
Miscellaneous	19	8
Total Concentrates, pounds	2,051	1,663
Pasture, animal unit days	13	..
Minerals, pounds	6	..
Labor, hours	14.1	10.9

a Illinois Bulletin 390, Feeds and labor per sow farrowing.
b Iowa Bulletin 294, Feeds and labor per animal in breeding herd.
c Skim milk is taken at its dry equivalent of .8 lb. per gal. in computing total pounds
of concentrates.

corn and oats and less tankage were fed, but the difference
was not great, except with the protein supplements.

The proportion of oats in the ration of the breeding
herd was much larger than that of the fattening pigs.
About one-sixth or one-seventh of the feed of the breed-

ing herd was oats, while the fattening pigs in Iowa had only one part of oats in twelve, and in Illinois one part in sixteen. The sows need less concentrated starchy material and can use bulkier feeds, while the pigs need

TABLE XXIX

FEED USED PER 100 LBS. GAIN ON PIGS AFTER WEANING

	ILLINOIS[a]	IOWA[b]
	McLean & Woodford Cos.	Humboldt Co.
Year of Study	1924-1926	1922-1924
No. Records	106	159
Pounds Gain per farm	19,409	14,395
Feeds:		
Corn, pounds	409	424
Oats, pounds	28	39
Other Small Grains, pounds	4	4
Mill Feeds, pounds	5	..
Tankage	13	5
Other Protein Feeds, pounds	6	..
Skim milk, gallons[c]	4	8
Total Concentrates, pounds	469	480
Minerals, pounds	1.5	.7
Pasture, animal unit days	1.9	..
Labor, hours	1.0	1.2
Average Weight Pigs When Sold, pounds	216	225

[a] Illinois Bulletin 390.
[b] Iowa Bulletin 294.
[c] In computing total pounds concentrates skim milk is counted at its dry equivalent of .8 lb. per gallon.

less bulk and more corn to gain weight. Such data as these are of great help in planning the livestock enterprises and fitting them to the available feed supply. Their use in the livestock budget will be taken up in the next chapter.

Table XXX
FEED USED PER YEAR BY A DAIRY COW

	MINNESOTA		IOWA	ILLINOIS[e]		NEW YORK[h]
	Jackson & Cottonwood Cos.[a]	Polk Co.[b]	Iowa Co.[d]	5,000 Pounds Production	7,000 Pounds Production	
Year	1921	1927	1925-1927			1927-1930
No. Farms	7	17	16	..	..	96
No. Cows per Farm	9.6	12.0	18.1	..	..	18
Total Animal Units	..	..	17.8	..	..	..
Corn, pounds	963	1,173	1,075	1,400	1,800	2,428
Small Grains, pounds	933		272			
Mill Feeds, pounds	..	92	69			
Oil Meal, pounds	36	11	..			
Tame Hay, pounds	596	870	1,800	2,000[f]	2,500[f]	4,000
Wild Hay, pounds	397	354				
Alfalfa, pounds	892	1,864		1,000[g]	1,000[g]	..
Corn Fodder, pounds	1,217	1,276				..
Corn Stalks, acres	..	..	1.2	..	..	..
Silage, pounds	2,365	3,985[c]	2,400	7,000	8,000	6,800
Pasture, days	215	168	..	175	175	..
Labor, hours	194	189	67	..	..	139
Pounds Milk Produced	4,841	..	..	5,000	7,000	7,536
Pounds Butterfat	186	190	131	..	..	..

[a] Minnesota Bulletin 205.
[b] Minnesota Bulletin 283.
[c] Includes silage, sugar beet tops, sugar beets, and potatoes.
[d] Iowa Bulletin 270.   Data in this column are per animal unit for the dairy herd.
[e] Illinois Bulletin 326.   Data from various cost studies.
[f] Legume hay or equivalent roughage.
[g] Non-leguminous roughage; straw and stover.
[h] New York State College of Agriculture (Cornell), mimeographed pamphlet: "Results of Cost Accounts on Livestock," by J. F. Harriott and L. M. Vaughan, 1931.

195

Feed Requirements of the Dairy Enterprise

The feed requirements of the dairy cattle differ with the productive capacity of the cows as well as with the feed supply available and the organization of the rest of the farm.   Table XXX shows the amounts of principal feeds consumed per dairy cow under five somewhat different sets of conditions.   The cows in Iowa were mostly

Fig. 36.—Where good pasture and roughage are available the dairy enterprise has an advantage.

dual-purpose cows—that is, on most of the farms milk was incidental to beef production.   Over 40 per cent of the income from the project was from beef sales.   In the New York study, on the other hand, the cows were definitely of the dairy type, and production per cow was over twice as high as in the Iowa study.   The Minnesota farms were between these two extremes in type and production.

Lower relative feed costs on high yield cows. The Iowa cows received about 1,400 pounds of concentrates, 1,800 pounds of hay, and 2,400 pounds of silage.   The New York cows, in contrast, received 2,800 pounds of concentrates, 4,000 pounds of roughage, and 6,800 pounds of silage. High-producing cows have the advantage in that their production rises more rapidly than their feeding

TABLE XXXI

RELATION OF MILK PRODUCTION PER COW TO COST AND RETURNS, 96 NEW YORK ACCOUNTS, 1927-1930

(From New York State College of Agriculture (Cornell), mimeographed pamphlet, "Results of Cost Accounts on Livestock," by J. F. Harriott and L. M. Vaughan, 1931)

	Low Third in Pounds of Milk per Cow	Middle Third in Pounds of Milk per Cow	High Third in Pounds of Milk per Cow
Production per cow, pounds.........	5,765	7,318	9,274
Cows per farm.....................	17.4	17.6	18.2
Value per cow, dollars..............	155	122	155
Grain per cow, pounds..............	1,755	2,371	3,160
Hay per cow, tons.................	1.8	2.1	2.0
Silage per cow, tons...............	2.4	3.4	4.3
Labor per cow, hours..............	120	142	153
Cost feed and bedding per cow, dollars	91.03	113.25	136.70
Labor and equipment per cow, dollars	63.57	75.63	82.71
Total cost per cow. dollars..........	198.30	223.60	263.36
Cost feed & bedding per 100 lbs. milk, dollars........................	1.58	1.55	1.47
Cost labor & equip. per 100 lbs. milk, dollars........................	1.10	1.03	.89
Total cost per 100 lbs. milk, dollars...	3.14	2.77	2.52
Returns per hour labor, dollars......	.22	.40	.54

costs and the overhead expenses increase even more slowly than expenses for feed. This is shown very well in Table XXXI.

When the farms are grouped on the basis of production, in Table XXXI, we find that the grain consumption averages 1,755 pounds for the cows whose production average was 5,765 pounds of milk per year. The farms

TABLE XXXII

MIXED OR DUAL-PURPOSE CATTLE ENTERPRISE, FEED AND LABOR USED PER ANIMAL UNIT PER YEAR

	Iowa[a]	Minnesota[b]
	Iowa Co.	*Cottonwood & Jackson Cos.*
Year...............................	1925-1927	1921
No. farms..........................	22	15
Animal units per farm...............	35.4	33
Feed per Animal Unit:		
Corn, bushels......................	21.6	16.0
Oats, bushels......................	5.7	} 350 (pounds)
Other concentrates, pounds..........	96	
Tame hay & alfalfa, pounds.........	} 1400	971
Wild hay, pounds..................		754
Silage, pounds.....................	2,400	2,178
Fodder, pounds.....................	....	455
Corn stalks, acres.................	1.8	....
Labor, hours........................	36.3	72
Value of product, beef, dollars.........	37.24	19.90
" " " dairy products, dollars.	12.64	19.02

[a] Iowa Bulletin 270.
[b] Minnesota Bulletin 205.

with the highest production averaged 9,274 pounds of milk and 3,160 pounds of grain per cow. This is an increase from 30 to 34 pounds of grain per 100 pounds of milk, and there is a similar change in the amount of silage used. The amount of hay declined per 100 pounds of milk, and the cost of labor, of course, increased much less rapidly than the production per cow. Shelter and equipment were used more economically by the higher-producing dairies. The combined results of these changes were a somewhat lower cost per 100 pounds of milk and a decided increase in returns per hour of labor used.

Feed Consumption in Dual-Purpose Herds

With dual-purpose herds it is possible to let the cows forage for more of their feed and to rough them through the winter. This means that less feed and labor is required than for dairy herds. Table XXXII shows feed consumption by herds of dual-purpose cattle in Iowa and southwestern Minnesota.

Some feeds are more plentiful in some localities than in others. More corn and less small grain was fed in Iowa than in Minnesota. For the same reason, more hay was fed in Minnesota and more cornstalks in Iowa. In the Iowa study, 21.6 bushels of corn plus 5.7 bushels of oats and 96 pounds of other concentrates were fed to each animal. In addition, the Iowa cattle each received 1,400 pounds of hay and the run of 1.8 acres of corn stalk fields.

Feed Consumed by Fattening Steers

Table XXXIII shows the average amounts of feed consumed per head and per 100 pounds gain by a large number of herds of fattening steers. The data included about 100 herds in each of five corn belt cattle-feeding areas for each of four years. These amounts vary with the age and weight of the cattle on feed, with the length of the feeding period, and with the character of the feeding place, whether they are fed in dry lot or on pasture.

Table XXXIII

FEED REQUIREMENTS UNDER DIFFERENT METHODS OF FATTENING CATTLE IN THE CORN BELT

(From U. S. Department of Agriculture, Technical Bulletin 23,
"Costs and Methods of Fattening Beef Cattle in the
Corn Belt," 1919-1923)

	Cattle Fattened in Dry Lot			Cattle Fattened on Grass	
	Strictly Dry Lot Fed	Fall Pastured	Summer Pastured	Carried Through Winter	Purchased in Spring
Days on farm	146	188	308	255	136
Daily gain, pounds	1.84	1.63	1.38	1.36	1.86
Weight when sold, pounds	1,092	1,100	1,104	1,149	1,134
Feed, per head:					
Corn, bushels	36.9	39.7	42.2	38.2	29.8
Protein meal, pounds	74	61	30	90	51
Prepared feeds & molasses, pounds	38	31	55	69	58
Legume hay, pounds	581	588	766	385	33
Mixed hay, pounds	167	177	338	180	76
Stover & straw, pounds	258	266	364	708	81
Silage, pounds	2,174	1,916	1,303	1,051	311
Pasture, days	3	55	161	160	130
By-products, per head:					
Pork, pounds	66	68	78	73	58
Manure, tons	3	3	3	1	..
Feed, per 100 pounds gain:					
Corn, pounds	768	726	559	616	660
Protein meal, pounds	28	20	7	26	20
Prepared feeds & molasses, pounds	14	10	13	20	23
Legume hay, pounds	216	192	181	111	13
Mixed hay, pounds	62	58	80	52	30
Stover & straw, pounds	96	87	86	204	32
Silage, pounds	808	626	308	303	123
Pasture, days	1	18	38	46	51
Labor per head, hours	10	10	11	19	6
Horse work, hours	6	7	8	12	7

These figures permit comparison with the actual performance on a given farm and they should help in planning the amount of feed necessary for a cattle-feeding

TABLE XXXIV

POULTRY—FEED USED

| | MINNESOTA | | IOWA[c] | NEW YORK[d] | |
	Cotton-wood and Jackson Cos.[a]	Polk Co.[b]	Iowa[c] Co.	Hens	Chicks
Year	1921	1927	1925-1927	1927-1930	1927-1930
No. Records	20	17	57	82	74
No. Chickens per farm	141	188	152	503	417
Feed per 100 chickens:					
Corn, pounds	1,820	230	4,516	}4,320	}1,200
Oats, pounds	1,301	}3,752	1,920		
Other small grains, pounds	191				
Mill feeds, pounds	80	146	1,880	3,740 mash	1,600 mash
Skim milk, gallons	94	246	365	..	..
Labor, hours	219	153	280	180	80
Eggs per hen	..	..	80	133	..

a Minnesota Bulletin 205, per 100 chickens.
b Minnesota Bulletin 283, per 100 chickens.
c Iowa Bulletin 270, per 100 hens.
d New York State College of Agriculture (Cornell), mimeographed pamphlet: "Results of Cost Accounts on Livestock," by J. F. Harriott and L. M. Vaughan, 1931.

project. Suppose a farmer were planning to buy a carload of cattle to be pastured a couple of months in the fall and then fed for four or five months in a dry lot. From the column in Table XXXIII headed "Cattle Fattened in Dry Lot: Fall Pastured" he can figure that he will probably need about 40 bushels of corn, 60 pounds of protein supplements, and 30 pounds of other feeds per head. If his cattle consume feeds ·at the average rate, he will need about 850 pounds of hay, 260 pounds of stover and straw, and 1,900 pounds of silage per steer. From the averages in Table XXXIII he would need to count on about 10 hours of labor per head during the feeding season.

If the cattle are kept through the winter and then fattened on pasture, the farmer will need slightly less corn and will probably use only about half as much silage. However, he would feed about 500 pounds of hay instead of 850, and could use 700 pounds of stover instead of 260.

Feed Requirements for Poultry

Like the various kinds of dairy enterprises, the poultry projects vary greatly in feed requirements. On some farms the poultry receive little feed except what they can pick up for themselves; on others, all feed is fed to them directly. On some farms the poultry enterprise is a very minor one; on others, it is the chief enterprise about which the rest of the farm business is organized.

References

Illinois Bulletin 261: "Cattle Feeding in Relation to Farm Management," by H. C. M. Case and K. H. Myers, 1925.

Illinois Bulletin 301: "The Place of Hog Production in Corn Belt Farming," by H. C. M. Case and Robert C. Ross, 1927.

Illinois Bulletin 329: "Organizing the Corn Belt Farm for Profitable Production," by H. C. M. Case, R. H. Wilcox, and H. A. Berg, 1929.

Illinois Bulletin 390: "Some Important Factors Affecting Costs in Hog Production," by R. H. Wilcox, W. E. Carroll, and T. G. Hornung, 1933.

Iowa Bulletin 242: "An Economic Study of the Cattle Feeding Enterprise in Iowa," by John A. Hopkins, 1927.

Iowa Bulletin 270: "The Livestock System in Iowa County," by J. A. Hopkins and R. S. Kifer, 1930.

Iowa Bulletin 294: "An Economic Study of the Hog Enterprise," by John A. Hopkins, 1932.

Minnesota Bulletin 205: "A Study of Farm Organization in Southwestern Minnesota," by George A. Pond and Jesse W. Tapp, 1933.

Minnesota Bulletin 270: "Factors Affecting the Physical and Economic Cost of Butterfat Production in Pine County Minnesota," by George A. Pond and Mordecai Ezekiel, 1930.

Minnesota Bulletin 283: "An Economic Study of the Livestock Possibilities of the Red River Valley of Minnesota," by George A. Sallee, George A. Pond, and C. W. Crickman, 1931.

Minnesota Bulletin 301: "Beef Production in Minnesota," by C. W. Crickman, George A. Sallee, and W. H. Peters, 1934.

New York State College of Agriculture (Cornell), mimeographed pamphlet: "Results of Cost Accounts on Livestock, 1927-1930," by J. F. Harriott and L. M. Vaughan, 1931.

Oregon Station Circular 94: "Cost of Producing Sheep on Western Oregon Farms," by Oran M. Nelson, 1929.

U. S. Department of Agriculture, Department Bulletin 1454: "Factors in the Cost of Producing Beef in the Flint Hills Section of Kansas," by R. H. Wilcox, W. E. Grimes, Morris Evans, and H. J. Henney, 1926.

U. S. Department of Agriculture, Technical Bulletin 23: "Costs and Methods of Fattening Beef Cattle in the Corn Belt." by R. H. Wilcox, R. D. Jennings, G. W. Collier, W. H. Black, and E. W. McComas, 1927.

CHAPTER XIV

Budgeting for the Livestock System

The Problem: How can we plan a livestock system that will fit in with the crop system and the other parts of the farm? How can we choose between two or three promising alternative systems?

Crop and Livestock Systems Should Conform To Each Other

We have already considered the functions which the livestock enterprises have in the farm business, their requirements for feed, labor, and other necessities. Our next problem is to fit the livestock projects into the rest of the farm organizations.

A study in Webster county, Iowa, showed that in that locality most of the corn was fed to hogs and the rest was fed to other livestock or sold for cash. There were a number of different ways of disposing of this remainder, as shown in Table XXXV. On some farms a large area of rough land which had to be kept in pasture made it necessary to keep a relatively large number of cattle. These were sometimes steers which were finished on part of the corn. Other peculiarities of the farm or of local marketing conditions, or even the farmer's preferences, sometimes determined the livestock project.

On farms that were level or gently rolling, there were three common ways of disposing of the corn crop. First,

on some farms, when little hay or pasture was raised, most
of the corn was fed to the hogs. Second, on some farms

TABLE XXXV

PRODUCTION AND DISPOSITION OF CORN IN A
CASH GRAIN AREA

(Webster Co., Iowa—1928-1930)

	Steer Feeding	Hog	Cash Grain		General Farms	
			120-199 acres	200-279 acres	120-199 acres	200-279 acres
No. Records.........	13	19	15	14	25	3
Av. acres in farm.....	204.7	159.6	147.8	237.7	153.8	241.5
Acres crops..........	161.8	133.8	120.9	201.0	124.0	200.8
Acres corn..........	79.7	69.2	63.0	104.3	60.0	108.1
Source of Corn:						
Raised, bushels[a]....	3820	3072	2822	4614	2724	4003
Bought, bushels....	1393	279	13	73	65	..
Disposition of corn:						
Sales, bushels......	588	308	782	1298	621	1005
Rent, bushels......	..	582	897	1728	321	608
Corn Fed:						
Hogs, bushels......	2033	1611	808	1063	1030	1725
Cattle, bushels.....	291	223	145	195	250	421
Steers, bushels.....	2114	129	25	57	87	474
Poultry, bushels....	73	104	105	117	146	118
Horses, bushels.....	99	108	116	200	120	141
Other, bushels......	40	..	3	..	13	11
Total Fed.....	4650	2175	1202	1632	1646	2890

[a] Quantities raised refer to preceding crop year—i. e., to years 1927-1929—while quantities bought and quantities fed refer to years 1928-1930.

much of the grain was sold and little livestock kept.
Third, a sort of compromise between these two plans
was developed, which resulted in a diversified or "general"
farm.

One important fact was that, in the Webster County study, the relative amounts of the important crops raised on hog, cash grain, and general farms were about the same. This shows that the kind and number of livestock depends largely on the individual farmer's choice.

The relative size of the different livestock enterprises will depend partly on the farmer's preference, but he should try to make the decision that will bring the greatest net profit. In order to figure out in advance what the returns from different livestock combinations will be, budgets similar to those for the crop enterprises should be worked out.

Data for the Livestock Budget

What data must we have in order to plan the livestock system? Four kinds of information will be needed. First, the available supply of feeds. Second, the approximate amounts of feed and other cost elements that will be needed per head or per 100 pounds of gain by the different kinds of livestock. Third, the rate of gain (in weight) or the yields of wool, milk, or eggs that can be expected. Fourth, we must have some estimate of the prices that these products will bring.

These necessary data are very similar to those we used in planning the crop program (Chapter IX). We do not need to discuss the available feed supply further at present. In the consideration of feed and other cost requirements, the data should be taken from that particular farm if possible. If not, from the farmer's own experience on some other farm. If he is a young farmer, without experience, or if he is considering some livestock project with which he is not acquainted, he will find his best sources of information in bulletins reporting cost studies in a similar area.

The farmer should be careful in selecting his source of information about a subject with which he is unacquainted, and conservative in interpreting it. Cost studies usually show the results obtained by experienced and rather skillful farmers. Records show quite a varia-

Fig. 37.—A frequent check-up on weights and numbers of livestock is worth-while.

tion in farmers' efficiency. Skilled livestock feeders may get daily gains fifty per cent greater than those obtained by the poorer feeders. The young farmer should not be disappointed if he does not get the maximum results for a year or so.

High rates of gain depend on other things besides feed. Raising pigs on clean ground, for example, may mean planning and extra work, but if this important step is left out, the effectiveness of all the other efforts may be destroyed.

FORM C
FARM BUDGET FORM
BUDGET FOR LIVESTOCK EXPENSES

	No.	Home Grown Feeds		Commercial Feeds			Other Expenses	
		Kind	Amount	Kind	Amount	Value		
Cattle:								
Milk Cows.........	10	Corn	500 bu.	Oil meal	2,000 lb.	$40.00	Vet., etc.	$20.00
		Hay	22½ (Ton)					
Other cattle.........	12	Oats	250 bu.	Bran	3,000 lb.	40.00		
Hogs:								
Sows...............	10	Corn	1,725 bu.	Tankage	2,000 lb.	50.00	Vet. & dip.	10.00
		Oats	360 bu.	Mineral	1,000 lb.	10.00		
		Skim milk	2,500 gal.					
Poultry.............	100	Corn	40 bu.	Mash	2,000 lb.	40.00	Misc.	5.00
		Oats	70 bu.					
Horses.............	5	Corn	125 bu.				Shoeing, Vet., etc.	10.00
		Oats	200 bu.					
		Hay	7½ ton					
Totals.............		Corn	2,300 bu.	Oil meal	2,000 lb.	180.00		$45.00
		Oats	880 bu.	Bran	3,000 lb.			
		Hay	30 ton	Tankage	2,000 lb.			
				Minerals	1,000 lb.			
				Mash	2,000 lb.			

A reliable estimate of prices likely to be received is very important in choosing projects and deciding about their sizes. The best sources of such information are the agricultural outlook publications issued annually by the U.S. Department of Agriculture and by most of the agricultural experiment stations. Similar outlook information is also published from time to time on the number of sows farmers intend to breed for spring and for fall pigs. Current reviews of cattle- and lamb-feeding and monthly statements on cold storage holdings of livestock products also give some basis for judgment on the course of prices. All available information on current production and the demand outlook should be carefully considered.

Livestock Budget Forms and Procedure

The livestock budget should be made up immediately after the crop budget and before the crops are actually planted, because each budget depends on the other. Perhaps the crops should be changed to provide more suitable feeds for the livestock and, on the other hand, the livestock must be made to fit in with the crops. During the winter, after the farm records of the previous year have been finished, is a good time to make up these budgets. Budgeting forms help to systematize this work and make it easier.

Let us make out a livestock budget for the farm for which we planned the crops in Chapter VI. This, you remember, is a 160 acre farm on which a young farmer is just moving. It has 30 acres of rough land in permanent pasture. The rest is tillable but apt to erode. The soil can be kept fairly productive by a five-year rotation, but corn should not be raised more than two years out of five.   The farmer decides to adopt a five-year rotation of corn-corn-oats-hay-pasture.   He expects to have available for feeding or sale 2,390 bushels of corn, 880 bushels of oats, and 30 tons of hay, besides 54 acres of pasture capable of supporting one cow or horse for each two acres.

This cannot all be used for productive livestock.   First we must take out feed for the five work horses needed to operate the farm.   The farmer figures that they will require about 125 bushels of corn, 200 bushels of oats, and $7\frac{1}{2}$ tons of hay.   These requirements are entered in the Budget For Livestock Expenses.

Because of the large acreage of pasture, the farmer will need to keep a good-sized herd of cattle.   He now has a small herd of Shorthorn cows and believes that a dual-purpose enterprise will be most profitable.   The horses will need about 10 acres of pasture, which leaves 44 for the cattle.   This pasture could be utilized by ten head of milk cows plus a couple of cows running with calves and additional young stock equal to ten animal units.

These 22 animal units of cattle would consume the $22\frac{1}{2}$ tons of hay which will remain after feeding the horses, besides the cornstalks which would be pastured by the dry stock.   The farmer's experience, supported by data on dual-purpose cattle in farm cost bulletins (see Chapter XIII), shows that these cattle would need about 500 bushels of corn and 250 bushels of oats.   The cows in milk and the fattening young stock (which are to be sold as yearlings) would need some additional protein supplements.   The farmer decides that a ton of linseed oil meal and a ton and a half of bran should be bought to supplement the farm raised feeds.   These commercial feeds are entered in the Budget For Livestock Expenses along with the farm raised feeds and the estimate of incidental cash expenses for veterinary bills and such items.

The rest of the corn and oats the farmer had intended to feed to about a dozen sows and their spring and fall litters. At this point he remembers that the poultry should be provided for. His wife thinks she could take care of 100 hens with little or no help from the men. These would make an addition to the farm income at small expense except for feed. They decide on this number and figure that 40 bushels of corn and 70 bushels of oats besides feeds picked up around the yards will be enough.

Adding up these figures, the farmer finds that horses, cattle, and poultry would require 665 bushels of corn, 520 bushels of oats, and all the hay. There remains 1,725 bushels of corn and 260 bushels of oats that could be fed to hogs. In addition, he estimates there will be about 2,500 gallons of skim milk for them. To make a satisfactory ration he decides to supplement these with a ton of tankage.

From experience, the farmer thinks he can count on raising 6 pigs per litter and selling them at 220 pounds each. This makes 1,320 pounds of live hogs per litter. If 500 pounds of feed were used per 100 pounds of gain, each litter would require 6,600 pounds of feed. When the amount of available feed is added up (counting skim milk at its dry equivalent of .8 pound per gallon), it totals 112,000 pounds. At 1,320 pounds per litter this is enough for 17 litters, or 22,400 pounds of live pigs.

This is somewhat disappointing, for the farmer had expected to raise more pigs. But the only way he could do so would be to buy both corn and tankage. After considering the outlook for corn and hog prices, he decides that, this year at least, it would be best to feed only what corn he raises. The number of spring and of fall litters is the next problem, and after considering his equipment he decides on 7 fall and 10 spring litters.

Fig. 38.—Farm scales and loading chute in a well arranged feedlot.

The crop of pigs, of course, may be either larger or smaller than anticipated. If there are more pigs they would have to be sold at lighter weights or more corn bought for them. If there were fewer, they could be fed longer, or the surplus corn sold as grain. His original intention of breeding 12 sows, with 12 spring and 8 to 10 fall litters, would have thrown the hog enterprise out of balance with the rest of the farm from the very start. Plans never turn out exactly, but it is well to look ahead as carefully as possible.

Summarizing Livestock Production

The next step, after planning the number of each type of livestock to be kept, is to estimate how much they will produce and the probable returns from them. This is done with the aid of the Budget For Livestock Production. Here again the farmer should use his own experience, as far as possible, added to and checked by published information on rates of gain. Prices he expects to receive should be estimated conservatively.

In the present case, the farmer expects to sell about eight yearlings and two cows a year. He thinks that prospects for prices the coming year are about $4 per hundred pounds for cows and $8 for the yearlings. At these prices the cows should bring in $80 and the yearlings $512. He expects also to produce 200 pounds of butterfat per cow. The family will use about 200 pounds as milk, cream, and butter. The income from the remaining 1,800 pounds is estimated at $540.

Similar methods are followed in estimating returns from other livestock. Amounts to be consumed on the farm are entered separately from amounts to be sold. The total values of home-used and marketed livestock products are finally added up and show that, in this example, the household will consume about $147 worth, while sales should bring in cash amounting to $2,937.

Choosing Between Alternative Budgets

Before the farmer carried out the plan we have just discussed, he of course considered other plans. This particular plan is only one possibility. One alternative would be to keep fewer cattle and add a flock of sheep. Another possibility would be to feed a carload of steers

Form D
Farm Budget Form

BUDGET FOR LIVESTOCK PRODUCTION

	Production		Used on Farm		Disposal		
	Kind	Amount			No.	Amount	Value
Cattle............	Cows	2 head	..	..	2	2000 lb.	$ 80
	Yearlings	8 head	..	..	8	6400 lb.	512
	Butterfat	2,000 lb.	200 lb.	$60	..	1800 lb.	540
Hogs............	Pork	22,400 lb.	600 lb.	42	99	21,800 lb.	1526
Poultry..........	Poultry	600 lb.	100 lb.	17	..	500 lb.	85
	Eggs	800 doz.	100 doz.	28	..	700 doz.	196
Total............	..	..	..	$147	..	..	

Prices assumed for livestock products:

Cows	@	$4.00 per cwt.	Hogs	@	$7.00 per cwt.
Other Cattle	@	8.00 per cwt.	Eggs	@	$ .28 per doz.
Butterfat	@	.30 per cwt.	Poultry	@	$ .17 per lb.

and keep only a few cows.   An even larger number of steers could be fed if some feed were purchased.

He should actually draw up at least a rough budget for three or four alternative plans.   Then he can choose the one which promises the greatest net return without over-taxing his resources or causing him to take unnecessary risks.

Notice that the livestock budget began in a sense where the crop budget left off.   On this particular farm the type of soil and the presence of the rough pasture land pretty well determined the crop system.   Still there was some choice.   Wheat or barley could have been raised instead of oats.   Had there been a silo, part of the corn might have been ensiled and fed to dairy cows in this form.   Or some land might have been limed and seeded to alfalfa, to reduce the necessary acreage of hay and allow changes in the crop rotation as well as the livestock system.

If low cattle prices had seemed likely, the farmer might have changed the crop system so he could raise more hogs.   In this case the rotation would have been recon-sidered and changed, possibly to a four-year rotation with part of the grass land cut for hay and part pastured, if fences permitted.   In this way the corn land would have been increased, with less pasture and hay.

References

Hopkins, John A., *Farm Records*, Collegiate Press, Ames, Iowa, 1936, Chapter II.

Idaho Bulletin 188: "Planning the Farm Business for the Year Ahead," by Paul A. Eke and Ezra T. Benson, 1932.

Illinois Bulletin 329: "Organizing the Corn Belt Farm For Profitable Production," by H. C. M. Case, R. H. Wilcox, and H. A. Berg, 1929.

Minnesota Bulletin 205: "A Study of Farm Organization in Southwestern Minnesota," by George A. Pond and Jesse W. Tapp, 1923.

Minnesota Bulletin 283: "An Eonomic Study of Livestock Possibilities in the Red River Valley of Minnesota," by George A. Sallee, George A. Pond, and C. W. Crickman, 1931.

South Dakota Bulletin 226: "Profitable Farming Systems for East Central South Dakota," by C. A. Bonnen and J. B. Hutson, 1927.

South Dakota Bulletin 249: "Economic Adjustments on Farms in Southeastern South Dakota," by R. H. Rogers, 1930.

U. S. Department of Agriculture, Farmers Bulletin 1564: "Farm Budgeting," by J. B. Hutson, 1928.

Part V

ECONOMIZING LABOR AND POWER

CHAPTER XV

The Field Layout

The Problem: How should the farm fields be laid out to economize labor and power? How can an unsatisfactory field layout be improved? What saving can be expected from reorganizing a poor layout, and how much expense would be justified in making the change?

Is the Field Layout Satisfactory?

A farmer moving to a new farm often finds the arrangement of the fields very unsatisfactory. Sometimes there are too many small fields, or they are of odd shapes that make short corn rows and slow up cultivation. Often the fields have not been planned with regard to the lay of the land and the corn rows run up and down hills, which causes erosion.

The farmer must decide whether it would pay to reorganize the field layout. How much would it cost and how much genuine advantage would be gained? Could a program be worked out for changing the layout gradually as old fences wear out? This would require relatively little extra expense, while an immediate change might be quite costly.

The defects of the field layout of a new farm will strike a farmer forcibly, while the same man might not be able to see such defects at all on the farm on which he had been living. Students in a farm management class at Iowa

State College were told to draw up maps of their fathers' farms and bring them to class with suggestions for their improvement. The maps were handed in with practically no criticisms. Then the teacher asked each student to criticize some other man's farm map. This time there were many suggestions for each farm. Each student could see the defects of other farms, but the one to which he was accustomed seemed to him quite satisfactory. We become so used to the organization we have that we simply cannot think of it any other way. This makes it all the more important for us to try to check up on our own farms, and in fact on ourselves. A list of the characteristics of a good field layout and a similar list of the common defects of such plans is very helpful in making this checkup.

Size and Shape of Field is Related to Economy of Labor

A well-planned farm is usually one that is laid out in a small number of large fields. The chief advantage of the large field over the small one is that it saves labor, particularly in the use of large-scale machinery.

How important is this saving? A study of farm layout at Cornell, by W. I. Myers, showed that it took about half again as long to plow an acre in a field of less than two acres as in a field of 15 or more acres. The smaller number of turnings, on the large field, which required about a half minute at the end of each furrow, was the most important time saver. The larger the field, however, the less important this saving became. A greater proportionate saving occurs as the size of the field is increased from 2 to 5 acres than when it is increased from 5 to 10 or from 10 to 15.

The same saving of labor occurred with rolling, drilling, mowing, or harvesting grain. This saving varied from one-fifth to two-fifths of the total labor requirement as the fields increased from less than two acres to 15 or more.

How large should the fields be?   This is determined by

Courtesy International Harvester Co.

Fig. 39.—Large rectangular fields permit the use of large capacity equipment and make for an efficient use of labor.

the size of the farm and the rotation of the crops. The number of fields should either equal the number of years in the rotation or else be a multiple of that number. In this way the whole of each field is in a single crop. This saves labor and temporary fencing.

What shape of field is most convenient and economical? To save labor in turning, the field should be rather long. There are two drawbacks to the use of very long fields, however. One is that it requires more fence per acre than a square field. The other is that the cross rows become too short in a very long, narrow field. A rectangular shape about three times as long as it is wide is a good compromise. Operations such as plowing can be run the long way. Corn cultivations and similar operations can usually be planned to be done more frequently the long way. The first and third cultivation of corn can be run lengthwise, while only the second crosses the field the short way.

Irregularly shaped fields waste labor. The sides of a field should be as nearly parallel as possible. Otherwise there are short rows along one or more sides, which means more labor in plowing or cultivating it. In most parts of the country the easiest way to lay out fields with right-angled corners and parallel sides is to base the field lines on road or line fences. In any case, the layout should allow the greatest possible number of fields to have their sides parallel.

Swampy Spots and Other Obstructions

Most farms have some obstructions, such as swampy spots, gullies, stumps, or piles of rock which interfere with cultivation. The farmer usually thinks of these as just so much lost land. The loss of the land is not the only loss involved.   Time and labor are lost in going across or around the obstruction.

These obstructions can often be removed with some labor and expense.   As the farmer considers the advisability of pulling out stumps, tiling an open ditch, or draining a wet spot, he should evaluate the future saving of labor as well as the value of the reclaimed land.   As a

Fig. 40.—Obstacles in a field cause unproductive work.

general rule we might say that the earning power of the reclaimed land and the value of the labor saved should yield a satisfactory return on the cost of the improvement.

Irregular Sizes of Fields

The number or the sizes of the fields do not always meet the requirements of the rotation.   A farmer who wants to adopt a four-year rotation may have six fields instead of four.   Or with 120 acres of crop land, his fields may run 28, 32, 25, and 35 acres instead of 30 acres each. It is expensive to tear down old fences and build new ones, and a reorganization of the field layout is likely to require several years. The expense may be kept down by using old fences as long as they last.

How can a four-year rotation be adopted in the meantime? One method is to use part of the largest field along with the smallest one in the rotation. Thus, if the 25 acre field is in oats, five acres of the 35 acre field would also be put in oats to bring the acreage up to the required 30. Of course there would still be variation between the 28 and the 32 acre fields, because it would not be worthwhile to put in a two-acre patch. If one field in the rotation were to be used for pasture, part of it could not be planted to a crop to be harvested. At best there will still be irregular acreages in the rotation.

Another arrangement might be to follow the rotation regardless of the size of the field in each crop, and then adjust the farm operations to the irregularities of production as well as possible. One year there might be 35 acres of hay and the next only 25. This would mean holding over part of one year's hay to the next in order to have a uniform supply.

Fences and Lanes

Fences are mainly for the purpose of confining livestock. Since fence is expensive, it should be used as economically as possible. This not only saves investment but allows us to use land to better advantage. Each fence occupies a strip of land that cannot be used for crop production. It may prevent plowing or cultivating a strip eight or ten feet wide. If large machinery is used, the wastage is even greater. In the cultivation of corn, potatoes, or other intertilled crops, the land required for turning adds further to this loss.

If a farmer intends to pasture stubble fields or has rotation pasture he will need to fence all fields in the rotation. The use of temporary fences often makes it possible to pasture or turn hogs on parts of fields. Temporary fences are advantageous if the general farm layout is to be changed in the near future. Steel posts which can be driven in and pulled out make it easier to put up or move fences. If the fence is to be permanent, the labor saved by the steel post should be compared with the saving from using home grown fence posts.

It does not pay to be too saving on fencing. An extra line of fence to make a lane will save time in driving live-stock to and from pasture. While square fields require the least fence, the longer, narrower ones save labor and time in taking care of crops.

Lanes. Where lanes are used, they should be wide enough to allow the larger pieces of machinery to be taken through them. Wide lanes do not become so muddy in wet weather, and animals are not so likely to be injured by crowding against the fences. Generally the lane should be wide enough so that it forms a part of the pasture itself. Two to four rods is a desirable width.

Lanes are sometimes laid out on a diagonal with the field lines in order to shorten the distance to the pasture. This is a mistaken economy because it results in irregularly shaped fields and short corn rows.

Gates should be located so that it is easiest to get to and from the fields, usually in the corner of the field nearest the barn. They should be strong but made as economically as possible. Slide gates are usually satisfactory for crop fields. Pasture or farmstead gates which are used daily should be hinged and made so they will swing easily. The post to which the gate is hung should be deeply planted and strongly braced. Gates should of course be wide enough to permit the passage of large pieces of machinery or loads of hay.

The Farmstead

The farmstead should be carefully planned, since it is the center both of the farm business and of the life of the farmer and his family. Obtaining the most satisfactory balance between efficiency of operation and pleasure and comfort in farm living is an exacting problem.

Capital invested in farm buildings and their surroundings often does not yield a satisfactory return as a business investment. This of course does not mean that we should not invest in buildings. The well-to-do farmer is quite justified in putting part of his earnings into things which increase the pleasure of living. The young or financially handicapped farmer is sensible in getting along with small or inexpensive buildings. This does not mean, however, that he should pay no attention to the requirements of comfort and sanitary living. Many of these comforts can be obtained with thought and planning and without much money. Financially successful farms often have small and inexpensive buildings.

Location of the farmstead. The farmstead should be located so that both fields and roads are easily accessible. Buildings placed far back from the road at the end of a long lane usually mean a waste of land and fencing. The most convenient and attractive dwellings face the road far enough away to avoid dust. Barns and feed lots should be behind the house, in such a direction that objectionable odors will be carried away by prevailing winds.

The most convenient location for the farmstead is on a road running through the middle of the farm. This ideal location is usually not possible, and the buildings must be set near a road along the edge of the farm. The convenience of a location near the road should be weighed against danger to persons and livestock from passing automobiles.

Buildings should be placed on a slight rise to secure good drainage. An elevation also gives a more pleasing view from the dwelling. The house should be on a higher elevation than, and about 150 feet from, the barn. Both the house and barns should be protected from prevailing winter winds by a windbreak. This saves fuel in the house and adds to the comfort of the livestock.

Size of the farmstead. How much land should be used for the farmstead? Myers found that on 53 New York farms the average area of the farmstead was 3.08 acres for farms which averaged 173 acres. Of this, buildings, lawns, and barnyards occupied 1.67 acres. The home orchard occupied .8 acre and the garden about .4 acre. There was .24 acre in paddocks and .32 acre of pasture in the orchard.

Buildings should not be crowded too close together, because of increased fire hazard and because barn odors become too noticeable around the house and the general appearance of the farmstead is less attractive. On the other hand, too widely scattered buildings are not efficient because they increase the number of necessary steps for the farmer and his helpers. The area that must be kept free of weeds by scythe and hoe is increased by widely scattered buildings. This sort of work adds nothing to the financial income. Another advantage of the small farmstead is that there is just that much more land available for crops.

The farmstead of ideal size, ideally located, is not usually awaiting the farmer who moves onto a new farm.

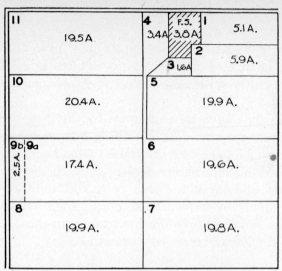

FARM No.1 - PRESENT LAYOUT
Farm Land   159.1 Acres
Roads   3.2 Acres

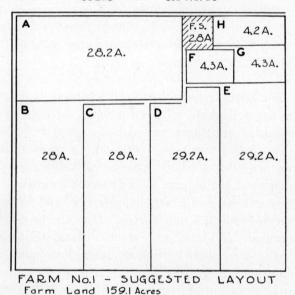

FARM No.1 - SUGGESTED LAYOUT
Farm Land   159.1 Acres
Roads   3.2 Acres   Old Fences ⎯⎯⎯⎯

Fig. 41.—Reorganization of fields on a level quarter section farm.

228

He can only change minor details and make more important changes gradually. Such changes as relocating feed or poultry yards may be very profitable and not very expensive.

Farms that have been occupied by the same man for many years are apt to have old feed lots, paddocks, and hog lots which have been divided into small pens and new lots added out of adjacent acreage until there is a large, unsightly, and unsanitary area which adds nothing to the income and is expensive to maintain. It is often cheaper and more satisfactory in the end to tear out this area and lay out simpler and more convenient feed yards.

Revising the Field Layout—A Level Quarter Section Farm

Let us apply these principles of field layout to three different farms. The first is a level farm of 162 acres, the second a farm of 79 acres, and the third a rough farm of 156 acres, badly cut up by a road, railroad, and streams.

The first farm, shown in Fig. 41, is divided into seven fields of approximately 20 acres each. An area of 20.8 acres is taken up by lots and pastures around the buildings. The owner wants to reduce the acreage of small pastures, establish a minor rotation of three years, and lay out the rest of the farm for a five-year rotation.

At the northeast corner are the farmstead and four small fields varying from 1.6 to 5.9 acres. It would be desirable to reorganize this area into a minor rotation that could be used for hog pastures, night pasture for horses, and similar purposes. This area could be more conveniently laid out in three small fields of about four acres each, to the east and south of the farmstead.

The five fields of the major rotation could be obtained by dividing the east side of the farm into two fields of 29.2 acres each. The western half could be divided into three fields of 28 acres each. This would require three

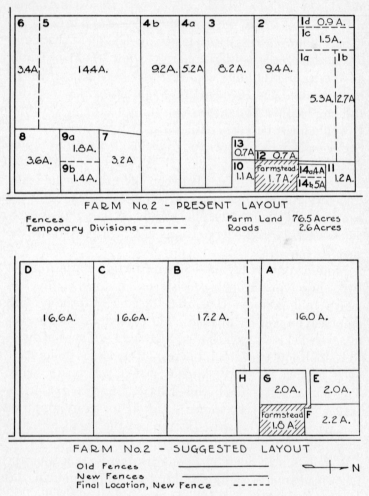

FARM No. 2 — PRESENT LAYOUT

Fences ————————— Farm Land 76.5 Acres
Temporary Divisions ------- Roads 2.6 Acres

FARM No. 2 — SUGGESTED LAYOUT

Old Fences —————————
New Fences —————————
Final Location, New Fence ------

Fig. 42.—Reorganization of fields on an 80-acre farm.

new lines of fence separating major fields and two short fences separating minor fields. Two new lanes would also be needed for access to the four south fields.

The new layout would require about 240 rods of fence. Would the added convenience be worth the extra expense if the present fences are in good condition? Fortunately, it may not be necessary to make the complete change at once. Establishing the minor rotation would probably be the most profitable change, since a large number of hogs is raised and the benefits of sanitation from rotating the hog pasture would add materially to the net income. It would likely be worth while to make this change at once. Six or eight rods of pipe would also be needed to provide water in field G.

Later on, as the fences between the major fields begin to deteriorate, new fences could be built in slack seasons to complete the plan. The plan should be drawn up as early as possible, so that every change can be a step in the desired direction.

Modification of layout—80 acre farm. Farm number two, shown in Fig. 42, consists of 79 acres of level or gently rolling land. It is used for general farming with emphasis on poultry raising. The present layout consists of seven fields of from 3.6 to 14.4 acres. There are also five small lots of .7 to 1.2 acres. The larger fields have been farmed in small patches instead of entire fields. The layout is to be simplified for a four-year major rotation. A four-year minor rotation for poultry yards, hog pasture, and so on is to replace the small lots surrounding the farmstead.

If four minor fields of about two acres each plus the farmstead are taken out of the 76.5 acres of farm land, this will leave about 66 acres. This would make four fields of

16.6 acres each.   The location of these fields will depend
on that of the minor fields.   If fields 11 and 14 are thrown
together they will make a minor field of 2.2 acres.   Fields
10 and 13 could form another if the fence at the west end
of 13 were moved a few rods to the west.   If this new
fence were extended to the north boundary of the farm,
the space so enclosed would be about 4 acres and could be
divided into the other two minor fields.

The remainder of fields 1 and 2 would amount to 16
acres and would serve, at least temporarily, as one of the
major fields.   The fields can ultimately be made the same
size if new field B is made as much larger than the desired 16.6 acres as field A falls short of that size.   Later
on, when it becomes necessary to replace the fence between these fields, they could be 16.6 acres as planned.

This reorganization would require about 120 rods of
new fence besides replacement of the fence between fields
A and B at some later date.   It would reduce the number
of fields from 14 to 8, which fits into definite rotations.

Reorganization of a rough quarter section farm.
Farm number three is shown in Fig. 43.   It consists of
145 acres, mostly rough land.   It is cut up by a road, a
railroad, and two streams.   On such a farm the layout
is dictated mainly by natural features and the roads.   In
this case, however, fields have been divided and sub-
divided until there are about 20 different fields or patches.

Let us first see which fields can be used in crop rotation.   At the eastern end of the farm there are four fields
which are level or gently rolling and have been in crops.
If fields 8a and 8b were thrown together and a few acres
added from field 9, this would give us three fields of about
equal size.   When it becomes necessary to renew the

fence between fields 4 and 7, it should be moved somewhat to the east to make these fields of equal size.

The western part of the farm is rougher and harder to deal with. At best the tillable acres can be divided only into irregular fields. Fields 5 and 6 could be thrown

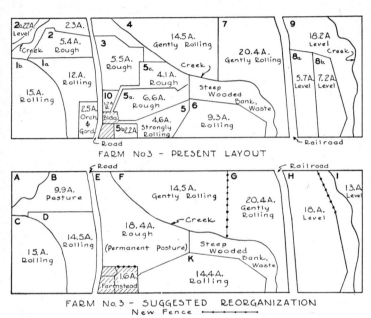

FARM No3 - PRESENT LAYOUT

FARM No.3 - SUGGESTED REORGANIZATION
New Fence

Fig. 43.—Reorganization of fields on a rough quarter section farm.

together to form one field of 14.4 acres. This land, although rolling, can be tilled if care is used and if it is not kept in crops too long at a time. Fields 1a and 1b are separated by a ravine which cannot be crossed with machinery. The new layout gives us three tillable areas and the rest of the farm should be kept in permanent pasture.

On this farm the problem is one of pulling down unnecessary fences instead of building new ones. Little new fence will be needed. Ultimately it would be desirable to move the orchard and garden from the west side of the road to the area east of the farmstead. This would make fields 1a, 1b, and 6 nearly equal in size. In the final plan the farm would consist of ten fields instead of the original 19. The rotation would require that two of the six fields be in corn each year; therefore, it would be desirable to alternate the smaller with the larger fields in the rotation. This would give about an equal acreage of corn each year.

References

New York State College of Agriculture (Cornell), Cornell Agricultural Experiment Station, Memoir 34: "An Economic Study of Farm Layout," by W. I. Myers, 1920.

U. S. Department of Agriculture, Farmers Bulletin 1132: "Planning the Farmstead," by M. C. Betts and W. R. Humphries, 1920.

CHAPTER XVI

Selecting Equipment to Economize Labor

The Problem: Which pieces of equipment should a farmer buy? How can he decide whether or not he needs a certain piece of equipment, such as a corn picker?

Choosing Farm Equipment

We often hear a farmer say that he is hampered by a lack of equipment; that if he had a mechanical corn picker, a combine, or some other machine, he could handle his farm with less labor. As soon as he saves some money he intends to buy more equipment. How can he decide what to buy and what to do without? His capital is nearly always limited, and it is important that he use it wisely in choosing machines.

Listing the Various Operations

What are the various jobs that will need to be done? This is the first problem in selecting equipment for the farm. Even on a farm that is already in operation there is an advantage in making a list of all crop operations. With such a list before him the farmer is better able to see the crop raising process as a whole and may be able to work out short cuts that will save labor and expense.

Such questions as the following should be answered. How many acres are to be plowed during the year? How many acres will be disced or harrowed? How many acres of grain will be harvested? How many days would a grain binder be used; how many for a combine? How many acres of corn are to be harvested? The answers may show definitely that certain pieces of machinery do not need to be purchased. Perhaps these pieces may be hired from neighbors. For other jobs the farmer may

Courtesy Wallace's Farmer-Homestead

Fig. 44.—Plowing cotton with one mule represents low labor efficiency.

have to choose between buying or hiring machines. For still others there may be a choice between using machinery or doing the work by hand. The rest of this chapter deals chiefly with the last two situations.

Diminishing Returns on Farm Equipment

The principle of diminishing returns appears again to help us decide how much capital should be invested in equipment. On a farm whose size could not be easily increased, one farmer with a definite supply of labor might profit from buying more machinery to save labor or do better work.   Another farmer in the same situation may now have more machinery than he needs, so that the capital already invested is not yielding a satisfactory return.   The first man is still in the stage of increasing returns from equipment, but the second man is in the stage of diminishing returns.

We may look at the same problem in another way. The farmer is generally limited in the amount of capital he has or can borrow.   This brings up again the question of opportunity cost.   If he spends too much for one purpose he has too little for something else.   If he invests in equipment until the last piece of machinery yields only 3 per cent on his investment, and neglects an opportunity to invest in livestock which would yield 8 per cent, he is not getting the maximum return from his resources.

Even if funds are available, it may be doubtful whether adding a mechanical corn picker, or a combine, or a grain drill on a small farm would increase the income by enough to cover depreciation and operating expenses, let alone yielding a satisfactory return on the investment.

Surveying Equipment Requirements of a Farm

Let us see how these principles will apply to a specific farm.   As an example we may consider the work to be done and the equipment available for it on a central Iowa farm of 317 acres.

There are 11 acres in roads and ditches, which leaves 306 acres of farm land.   Last year there were raised 157 acres of corn, 91 acres of oats, 6 acres of alfalfa, and 44 acres of bluegrass pasture.   It is mostly a grain farm, but the farmer is working toward a dairy enterprise.   He has

9 cows, 9 heifers, and 4 yearlings. There are 15 sows and 85 spring pigs, and a small poultry flock of 100 hens. The power has been furnished by 7 horses and an old tractor valued at $100. There are 3 colts. The work has been done by the farmer himself, working full time, about 9 months of hired help, and the farmer's father,

Courtesy Minneapolis-Moline Power Implement Co.

Fig. 45.—The two-row cultivator represents a big improvement in the use of labor over that shown in Fig. 44.

who works mostly at chores and other light work, doing an equivalent of about 4 months' work per year.

Which crop operations will require machinery? The 157 acres of corn were plowed once and disced twice. Of the corn land, 114 acres were harrowed once, 23 acres harrowed twice, and 20 acres three times. The corn was planted with a two row planter and cultivated three times, except for 11 acres which were cultivated a fourth time. The corn was picked by hand.

The 91 acres put in oats were disced twice, then planted with an endgate seeder. They were harrowed once and harvested with an 8-foot binder.

Adding up the crop work, we find that 157 acres were

Courtesy J. I. Case Co.

Fig. 46.—Discing and harrowing in one operation makes efficient use of labor.

plowed, 496 acres were disced, and 311 acres were harrowed. Corn cultivation amounted to 482 acres, and 91 acres of oats were harvested. In addition, there were three cuttings on 6 acres of alfalfa.

What equipment is available to do this work? The list in Table XXXVI shows that the farm is well equipped. Most of the machinery is so old, however, that it will soon

Table XXXVI

EQUIPMENT ON A 317-ACRE IOWA FARM

	Years of Life Remaining	Value	Annual Depreciation (Nearest Dollar)
Crop Equipment:			
Gang plow................	12	$ 14	$ 1
Sulky plow...............	4	5	1
Cultivators, two, 2-row.......	5	45	9
Cultivators, two, 1-row.....	6	42	7
Binder, 8-foot............	4	64	16
Mower, 6-foot.............	4	16	4
Manure spreader...........	7	44	6
Wagons, 3................	6	115	19
Seeder, endgate...........	9	22	2
Hay loader...............	4	8	2
Rake, half interest.........	14	10	1
Elevator..................	15	150	10
Discs, two, 8-foot..........	8	98	12
Harrow, 18-foot............	4	8	2
Spring wagon..............	5	20	4
Total Crop Machinery....		$661	$ 96
Livestock Equipment:			
Cream Separator...........	11	$ 23	$ 2
Hog troughs..............	..	3	..
Brooder and houses........	14	14	1
Tank heater...............	2	2	1
Hog oiler.................	10	10	1
Total Special Livestock Equipment...		$ 52	$ 5
Miscellaneous Equipment:			
Harness, 5 sets............	4	$60	$15
Small Tools...............	..	40	..
Ford Truck...............	4	155	39
Tractor..................	2	100	50
Total Equipment........		$1068	$205

be necessary to replace it.   This may prove to be an advantage, since it will provide an incentive to revise the general equipment layout.   Much of the equipment could be replaced with very little loss from junking the machinery on hand.   The total value of crop equipment, including wagons, is found to be $661.   The small amount of special livestock equipment is valued at only $52.   The total value of equipment, including a tractor and truck, is $1068.

Expenses Involved in the Use of Equipment

What expenses are involved in the use of crop equipment?   First, depreciation must be considered.   The machines are growing older every year and it will soon be necessary to replace them.   If we divide the present value of each machine by the number of years it is expected to last, and add the results, we find that the total yearly depreciation is $96.

Interest on the investment is another important expense.   At 7 per cent this amounts to $46.   The third item is for repairs and upkeep.   Repairs vary greatly from year to year and with the age of the machine.   On this farm repairs and new parts for equipment cost $78 the past year.   In all, these three items amount to $220, or 86 cents per acre of crops raised.

How does this expense compare with corresponding figures from other farms?   Table XXXVII shows that the total crop equipment expense amounted to $2.49 per acre for farms of 160 or more crop acres in Iowa County, Iowa, in 1925-1927.   The three items of depreciation, interest, and repairs made up about 60 per cent of the total.   Other items were oil and grease, labor in repairing or taking care of machinery, shelter, and miscellaneous expense.

Low equipment expense on this 317 acre farm does not necessarily mean that the farmer is getting the most for his money. The purpose of machinery is to save labor and reduce expense in the operation of the farm as a whole. If the farmer does not have all the machinery

TABLE XXXVII

ANNUAL EXPENSES ON EQUIPMENT

Iowa County Cost Route, 1925-1927
(From Iowa Bulletin 264.)

Size of farm, crop acres...........	40-79	80-119	120-159	160 & up
Average crop acres..............	53.9	87.7	140.5	202.3
Crop Equipment:				
Depreciation.................	$ 60	$ 90	$105	$184
Repairs......................	9	12	26	38
Interest.....................	40	63	64	88
Oil and grease................	1	1	2	3
Labor.......................	19	32	40	59
Shelter......................	35	22	34	66
Miscellaneous................	24	25	35	65
Total crop equipment........	$188	$245	$306	$503
Livestock Equipment:				
Depreciation.................	$ 25	$ 34	$ 59	$ 69
Repairs......................	8	3	5	10
Interest.....................	16	18	20	20
Labor.......................	3	11	6	10
Miscellaneous................	4	6	6	12
Total livestock equipment....	$ 56	$ 72	$ 96	$121
Total equipment expense...	244	317	402	624
Equipment Expense, per crop acre:				
Crop equipment..............	$ 3.45	$ 2.79	$ 2.17	$ 2.49
Livestock equipment..........	.64	.64	.50	.25
Harness, etc.................	.40	.17	.26	.35
Total equipment............	$ 4.49	$ 3.60	$ 2.93	$ 3.09

needed, or if some of it is in poor condition, his saving in this direction may be offset by a loss in another. Let us come back to the question of the equipment needs of this particular farm.

Selecting Equipment to Save Labor

If we check over the seasonal use of labor on this farm we shall see that there are two serious peaks during the year. The first is from about April 20 until the corn is laid by in July. During this period the farmer has to prepare the seed beds and plant corn and oats. Then he has to cultivate corn and in between times cut and haul alfalfa. The second labor peak is in the fall, at corn-picking time. Most of the hired labor has been needed during these two periods. Would it be possible to reduce one or both of these labor peaks by changing equipment?

The choice between horses and tractors as a source of motive power is to be studied later, but it is an important consideration on this farm. There are seven work horses and an old tractor. The tractor has been used for plowing and discing. There is no four-row corn planting or cultivating outfit to go with the tractor. When this old tractor is turned in on a new one, the farmer should consider a general purpose type of tractor that can be used in cultivating corn as well as in plowing or discing. With such a tractor he could take care of his 157 acres of corn with the help of one man and would reduce labor requirements during this period.

Machinery for peak seasons. How much labor could be saved by using a four-row instead of a two-row cultivator? The four-row cultivator operates about twice as fast as the two-row one. With two-row cultivators it would take three men with four-horse teams about five eight-hour days to cover 157 acres of corn. With one four-row tractor outfit and one two-row horse outfit the same work would require only two men for the same length of time.

The second labor peak occurs at corn-picking time. The farmer has been hiring three extra men for six weeks or two months. Would it pay him to get a mechanical corn picker? A method of comparing the probable costs of picking by hand and by machine will be discussed in the next section.

Except for these two jobs, corn cultivating and corn picking, the farm seems adequately equipped. These peak labor loads are the ones that should be studied most carefully. On a wheat farm the peak load would occur at harvest time and the advisability of buying a combine would be the problem there. Other types of farms have still different problems. These peak season jobs are the ones for which new or large capacity machinery should be considered. Little except leisure would be gained by the use of such machinery during slack seasons.

Estimating the Advantage of Buying a Machine

Would a mechanical corn picker be a good investment for the farmer we have been discussing? How can he compare the advantages of machine and hand picking? The first step is to draw up and compare estimates of the expenses of using the machine and of hand picking.

Four different kinds of expenses must be considered for the mechanical picker. First are the expenses of the machine itself. Second, the cost of the power to operate it. Then the cost of labor and also of horses and wagons used in hauling corn to the crib must be considered.

Not all these expenses will vary with the amount of corn picked or with the method of picking. For example, wagons are usually available on the farm and there is very little difference in their annual cost whether they are used six weeks for hand picking or two weeks for machine picking. This is also true for horses and for the farmer's own labor, unless there is some other profitable work they could be doing if they were not picking corn.

The largest expense on the machine will be for depreciation. This is hard to determine at the time the machine is bought. Considering the possibility of the machine's becoming out-of-date or obsolete, 10 per cent seems a reasonable estimate. This item averaged $62 per year on the 40 corn pickers studied in 1931.

Interest will probably be the next largest item. In the study tabulated in Table XXXVIII, this was figured at 7 per cent on the average investment in the machine during its life—that is, on half its first cost. It amounted to $21.70. The expense for shelter of the machine was taken arbitrarily at 2 per cent of the purchase price, $12.40. These three items—depreciation, interest, and shelter—make up the overhead on the machine and will vary but little with the amount it is used, unless this exceeds 500 or 600 acres per year.

The amount of repairs necessary will vary with the amount of work done. In the Iowa study it amounted to between one and two cents per acre of corn picked. Two cents seems enough under ordinary conditions.

On the tractor, 40 cents per hour should cover depreciation, repairs, and interest. Since it took about .6 hour to pick an acre of 40-bushel corn, these items will amount to about 24 cents per acre. Fuel, oil, and grease add an-

TABLE XXXVIII

ESTIMATED COSTS OF PICKING CORN

Based on Data from 40 Iowa Farms, 1931

Assumed yield 40 bushels per acre

Acres of Corn Harvested	100	200	300	400	500
COSTS WITH MECHANICAL PICKER:					
Expenses on Corn Picker:					
Depreciation and Obsolescence @ 10%	$ 62.00	$ 62.00	$ 62.00	$ 62.00	$ 62.00
Interest on average value @ 7%	21.70	21.70	21.70	21.70	21.70
Housing for picker	12.40	12.40	12.40	12.40	12.40
Repairs to picker, 2 cents per acre	2.00	4.00	6.00	8.00	10.00
Expense on Tractor:					
Fuel, oil, and grease	18.00	36.00	54.00	72.00	90.00
Tractor depreciation & repairs @ 40 cents per hour	24.00	48.00	72.00	96.00	120.00
Labor, 1.6 hours per acre @ 20 cents per hour	32.00	64.00	96.00	128.00	160.00
Horse work, @ 10 cents per hour	32.00	64.00	96.00	128.00	160.00
Wagons @ 5 cents per hour	8.00	16.00	24.00	32.00	40.00
Total cost of machine picking	$212.10	$328.10	$444.10	$560.10	$676.10
COSTS OF PICKING BY HAND:					
Labor, @ 3 cents per bushel	$120.00	$240.00	$360.00	$480.00	$600.00
Horse work*	32.00	64.00	96.00	128.00	128.00
Wagons*	8.00	16.00	24.00	32.00	40.00
Total cost of hand picking	$160.00	$320.00	$480.00	$640.00	$800.00
COMPARISON OF VARIABLE COSTS:					
Machine picking (repairs, fuel, grease, labor)	$ 76.00	$152.00	$228.00	$304.00	$380.00
Hand picking, labor @ 3 cents	120.00	240.00	360.00	480.00	600.00

* The same total charges are used for horses and wagons for hand picking as for machine picking.

other 17 or 18 cents, making the total tractor expense about 42 cents per acre.

Labor cost must be added next.   An average of 1.6 hours of labor were required to pick and haul an acre. At 20 cents per hour this makes 32 cents per acre.

Some costs do not vary with method used.   The expense of using horses and wagons, as was mentioned

Table XXXIX

COMPARING HAND AND MACHINE CORN PICKING COSTS

Cost with Mechanical Picker on 157 Acres:

Depreciation, interest, and shelter	$96.10
Repairs, at 2 cents per acre	3.14
Expenses on tractor:	
Fuel, oil, and grease @ .18 per acre	28.26
Tractor depreciation and repairs, @ .40 per hour	37.68
Labor, 1.6 hours per acre @ .30	75.36
Horse work, @ .15 per hour	75.36
Wagons @ .05 per hour	12.66
Total cost, machine picking	$328.56

Costs of Picking by Hand:

Labor @ .04½ per bushel	$282.60
Horse work (as above)	75.36
Wagons (as above)	12.66
Total cost of hand picking	$370.62

above, will be about the same for both methods.   They are already on the farm and using them more will not add much to the expense.   The same costs can therefore be used in figuring both methods.

The expense of machine picking per acre or per bushel will of course be lower with a large acreage because this will spread the overhead more thinly, as is shown in Table XXXVIII.   When hand picking can be hired for three cents per bushel, the cost of machine and hand picking is about equal for 200 acres of corn.   On a smaller acreage the advantage is with hand picking. If the relative prices of the machine, tractor labor, or horse work change, this also changes the point of marginal advantage for the machine.

Comparing hand picking with machine costs. Suppose hand picking were 4½ cents per bushel while daily labor was 30 cents per hour, horse work 15 cents, and the other elements of expense the same as in Table XXXVIII. Would it be profitable for our farmer with 157 acres of corn to buy a mechanical picker? The answer may be worked out in the following manner.

With these rates mechanical picking would be about $40 cheaper, provided there is not some offsetting disadvantage.

Non-Financial Considerations Are Often Important

The advantages or disadvantages of a certain machine cannot always be measured directly in financial terms. The corn picker will also get the work done earlier, and thus leave the farmer more time to do fall plowing, repair fences, and get ready for winter. Another advantage of the picker, which will appeal particularly to the farmer's wife, is that the trouble of hiring men and boarding them is avoided.

On the other hand, the machine knocks off some ears and shells some corn. In the Iowa study, fields on 12 farms were gleaned after the machine, and about 4 bushels per acre obtained. Gathering this corn required an average of 1.1 hours of labor and 1.3 hours of horse work per acre. Hand huskers, however, also miss some corn, perhaps two or three bushels per acre. Another disadvantage of the machine is that it knocks down the stalks and injures the stalk pasture. This loss is increased if snow or rainy weather follows corn picking. Machine picking is less adaptable to adverse conditions, such as wet, muddy ground.

Most of these disadvantages can be partly overcome. Proper adjustment of the machine two or three times a day greatly reduces the loss of corn. If cattle and hogs can be turned into the field just after the machine, they will get most of the dropped corn. Stalk pasture is available much earlier than with hand picking and is more valuable because the stalks have not dried out so much.

All of these points should be considered by the farmer when he decides that the various advantages, financial and otherwise, justify his investment in the machine. The financial figures are necessary for an intelligent decision, but they are by no means the only consideration.

References

Hopkins, John A., *Farm Records*, Collegiate Press, Ames, Iowa, 1936, Chapter XIX.

Illinois Bulletin 373: "Harvesting the Corn Crop in Illinois," by P. E. Johnson and K. H. Myers, 1931.

Iowa Bulletin 260: "Life, Service and Cost of Service of Farm Machinery," by J. B. Davidson, 1929.

Iowa Bulletin 264: "Horses, Tractors and Farm Equipment," by John A. Hopkins, 1929.

Iowa Agricultural Experiment Station, Mimeographed publication by Agricultural Economics Section: "The Mechanical Corn Picker—Utilization and Cost of Use," by John A. Hopkins, 1932.

Indiana Bulletin 362: "Mechanical Corn Pickers in Indiana," by L. G. Hobson and R. H. Wileman, 1932.

Michigan Special Bulletin 241: "A Farm Management Study of Crop Production Practices," by P. G. Minneman and E. B. Hill, 1933.

Minnesota Bulletin 256: "The Combine Harvester in Minnesota," by A. J. Schwantes, G. A. Pond, A. C. Arny, C. H. Bailey, R. H. Black, L. A. Reynoldson, and W. R. Humphries, 1929.

South Dakota Bulletin 244: "The Use of the Combine in South Dakota," by Gabriel Lundy, K. H. Klages, and J. G. Goss, 1929.

U. S. Department of Agriculture, Technical Bulletin 244: "Harvesting Small Grains, Soybeans, and Clover in the Corn Belt with Combines and Binders," by L. A. Reynoldson, W. R. Humphries, and J. A. Martin, 1931.

U. S. Department of Agriculture, Farmers Bulletin 1565: "Shall I Buy a Combine?" by L. A. Reynoldson, J. H. Martin, and W. R. Humphries, 1928.

U. S. Department of Agriculture, Farmers Bulletin 1715: "Methods and Costs of Husking Corn in the Field," by Kenneth H. Myers, 1933.

CHAPTER XVII

Selecting the Type of Power—Horses or Tractor

The Problem: Should the farm obtain its motive power from horses or from a tractor? Which provides the cheaper power? What are the advantages and disadvantages of each? How is the choice affected by the type and size of farm?

What Are the Power Requirements of the Farm?

One of the hottest debates in recent years has been between the advocates of horses and those of tractors as sources of farm power. Evidently there has been an advantage with the tractor, since the number of horses has been declining for about twenty years, while the number of tractors has increased almost continuously. Horse breeders reply that a large part of the shift to tractors has been a mistaken one. In evidence of this they point to the change back to horses during the depression of the early 1930's, when many tractors stood idle because their owners decided it would not pay to buy fuel and oil for them.

Before choosing the type of power, the jobs to be done with it should be checked over carefully. The type of power which promises to be most economical is the one that should be chosen. The combined labor, power, and equipment outfit should be the one that will do the best work at the least cost.

Which farm operations require power? Most important are those which take power to pull the machines. Plowing and discing require the most power. Jobs which need less motive power are harrowing, rolling, crop planting, cutting grain and hay, and hauling.

There is also belt work to be done in threshing, grinding feed, and sawing wood. Here mechanical power is the only choice. Belt work may be done by the tractor, a stationary engine, or an electric motor, if current is available. More than one type of power is needed on nearly every farm. Our real problem is not to decide on one source of power, but to choose a combination of two or three and to select the job to be done by each.

The Peak Season Determines the Power Requirement

How many horses or how large a tractor will be needed? The amount of power needed during the busy seasons rather than the total amount of work to be done during the year determines the answer. On a specialized grain farm, two complete power outfits may be needed for a month or six weeks when the seedbed is prepared and the crop planted. Then there may be little to do until harvest, when two outfits may again be busy for long hours each day for three or four weeks. Perhaps these outfits are used only three or four months during the year. It is necessary, however, to invest in as many tractors or horses as will be needed during the busy seasons and to keep them during the entire year.

A crop of corn and a crop of small grain can usually be raised with about the same number of horses as would be needed to raise either one alone.   This is true because the rush seasons on one do not coincide with those of the other.   The number of horses or of tractors is determined by the peak load requirements of the *combined* enterprises, not of the individual ones.

Fig. 47.—The big team hitch furnishes power to compete with tractors.

Relative Advantages of Horses and Tractors for Farm Work

What are the principal advantages of each type of power?   Horses are often raised on the home farm with little actual cash investment.   This does not mean that colts cost nothing.   If they were not raised there would be more feed for cattle or other livestock which would yield salable products. Their cost is, therefore, an opportunity cost rather than a direct outlay. Work horses require few cash expenses, since they eat home-raised feed.

Horses have the advantage of being adaptable, in that they can be worked in large teams for plowing and used in pairs or singly for hauling or other light work. They can also be used under unfavorable conditions, as on wet, muddy ground where the tractor would bog down. Hired helpers can usually manage horses better than tractors, and there are also likely to be mechanical difficulties with the tractor.

On the other hand, the large amount of power furnished by the tractor is a distinct advantage with such jobs as plowing or discing. A man's time can be used more efficiently because of the greater power and larger machines used with the tractor. He can take care of a greater acreage of crops with the same amount of labor or he can get along without part of the help he has been hiring.

The tractor moves faster than horses in the field. With a tractor the man can accomplish more in a day not only because he can use larger machines but also because he can cover the ground more rapidly. The tractor is not bothered by heat or flies and can work as many hours per day as the farmer cares to keep it in operation. This is important in rush seasons and particularly at grain harvest.

Costs of Horse Work

What does it cost to keep a horse for a year? A number of studies have been made on this question. The most extensive was probably the one made in five corn belt states in 1929-30 and reported in U.S. Department of Agriculture Technical Bulletin 384. This study permits

a comparison of costs between farms with horses worked
in ordinary sized teams, big hitch horse farms, farms with

TABLE XL

AVERAGE QUANTITIES OF FEEDS USED FOR
HORSES PER HEAD

Eleven Areas in Five Corn Belt States, 1929.
(From U.S. Department of Agriculture Technical Bulletin 384)

	Ordinary Horse Farms	Big Team Hitch Farms	2 and 3 Plow Tractor Farms	General Purpose Tractor Farms
No. Horses in Study	2067	379	1632	347
Concentrates:				
Corn, bushels	30.9	27.0	27.3	29.2
Oats, bushels	48.9	52.6	49.4	42.0
Total pounds grain	3313	3193	3115	3007
Roughage, tons:				
Legume hay	.5	.7	.6	.5
Mixed hay	.6	.5	.7	.6
Non-legume hay	.5	.4	.5	.8
Straw and Stover	.8	1.1	.9	.7
Total roughage	2.4	2.7	2.7	2.6
Pasture, months:				
Grass	4.4	4.2	3.9	4.8
Corn-stalks	1.6	2.2	1.5	1.6
Grain stubble	.1	.3	.1	.1
Total pasturage	6.1	6.7	5.5	6.5

the old or "ordinary" type of tractor, and those with the
general purpose type of tractor.

Table XL shows that the average ration for work horses
in this study contained about 30 bushels of corn and

slightly under 50 bushels of oats per year.   The big hitch farms fed a little over 50 bushels of oats and the ordinary horse farms slightly more than 30 bushels of corn besides other feed.

These farms also fed from 2.5 to 2.7 tons of roughage besides the grain.   Of this amount about one-half ton each was of legume hay, mixed hay, and non-legume hay. The rest was mostly straw and corn stover.   The horses also received between four and six months of blue grass pasturage and about two months in stalk fields.

What were the values of this feed and of the other cost elements used by horses?   Table XLI shows the average values of feed from $71 to $78 at 1929 prices.   Labor in taking care of the horses was the next largest cost element. This amounted to between 60 and 75 hours, except on the big hitch farms, where there was some saving in taking care of a larger number of horses.   There the average was 46 hours per horse.   At 1929 prices this labor cost amounted to about $15 per horse, except on the big hitch farm, where it was around $11.

Other variable costs are for bedding, shoeing, veterinary, and harness charges.   Fixed charges are for depreciation of the horses and interest on the investment in them.   The total of all costs averaged about $100 at 1929 price levels.   Credits for colts and for manure should be deducted from this total cost, about $12 per horse.   The average net cost per horse was $86 on big hitch farms and from $89 to $96 in the other groups.

The cost per hour of horse work on these farms varied from 13.9 to 14.5 cents on four of the five groups.   On the big hitch farms it was only 11.8 cents per hour.

There are limits to the significance of these figures. They assume that it is possible to place valuations on all

Table XLI

AVERAGE COST OF USING HORSES ON THE HOME FARM

Eleven areas in five corn belt states, 1929.

(Data derived from United States Department of Agriculture
Technical Bulletin 384)

	2 Plow Tractor Farms	3 Plow Tractor Farms	General Purpose Tractor Farms	Ordinary Horse Farms	Big Team Hitch Farms
Horses per farm.........	5.4	6.7	4.4	6.0	11.2
Hours Horse work, home farm................	3352	4499	2816	4146	8208
Chore work on horses, hours...............	352	391	284	389	524
Crop acres per farm.....	184	226	196	137	252
Costs per horse:					
Chore work..........	$ 16.22	$ 14.53	$ 16.05	$ 15.23	$ 10.99
Feed...............	71.49	75.41	74.24	77.69	75.44
Bedding............	3.83	3.91	3.96	3.99	3.95
Shoeing.............	.51	.44	.43	.56	.09
Vet. & medicine.......	.66	.63	.70	.63	.69
Harness charge.......	2.48	2.50	2.52	2.21	1.45
Total variable cost..	$ 95.19	$ 97.42	$ 97.90	$100.31	$ 92.61
Depreciation.........	..	$ 2.10	$ .19	$ 2.06	$ .15
Interest..............	$ 5.80	6.32	5.83	5.90	6.75
Total Fixed cost....	$ 5.80	$ 8.42	$ 6.02	$ 7.96	$ 6.90
Total of all costs....	100.99	105.84	103.92	108.27	99.51
Credits:					
Colt.................	$ .89	$ 1.19	$ 2.05	$ 1.64	$ 3.78
Manure.............	10.49	10.44	9.56	10.63	9.20
Total credits.......	$ 11.38	$ 11.63	$ 11.61	$ 12.27	$ 12.98
Net cost per horse.......	$ 89.61	$ 94.21	$ 92.31	$ 96.00	$ 86.53
Net cost per farm.......	483.88	631.21	406.16	576.00	969.14
Net cost per horse hour..	.145	.111	.144	.139	.118
Net costs at 1931-'32 prices:					
Net cost per horse.....	$ 48.50	$ 52.30	$ 49.56	$ 52.08	$ 46.89
Net cost per farm.....	261.87	350.36	218.09	312.47	525.35
Net cost per horse hour	.079	.079	.078	.076	.064

the cost elements.   Actually it is not possible to evaluate such items as stalk pasture or the farmer's own labor. It would not be possible to find a market for them or to sell them without upsetting the farm operations.   The values just given are at 1929 price levels.   At 1931-32

Courtesy of John Deere Co.

Fig. 48.—The old, heavy type of tractor provided plenty of power but could be used only for a few operations.

prices these costs would be about 45 per cent lower, as is shown at the bottom of Table XLI.

Cost of Tractor Operation

Tractor cost figures are shown in Tables XLII and XLIII.   In figuring such costs we must know first the amounts of fuel, oil, and grease used per hour while the tractor is running.   From these basic physical data, estimates of financial costs can be quickly made from the current prices.

Table XLII shows that, on the farms studied by the U. S. Department of Agriculture, an average of 1.9 gallons of fuel was used per hour of drawbar work by two-plow

Courtesy John Deere Co.

Fig. 49.—The light, general purpose tractor is adaptable to a wide variety of uses.

tractors.   Besides fuel, the tractors required an average of .08 gallon of lubricating oil and .043 pound of grease. For three-plow tractors the corresponding figures were 2.6 gallons of fuel, .10 gallon of oil and .046 pound of grease.   General purpose tractors used a little less of each than the ordinary two-plow tractor.   On belt work the fuel used per hour was about ten per cent less than for drawbar work.

Total Operating Costs for the Tractor

How much does it cost to operate the tractor for a year? On these farms the two-plow tractors were used an average of 301 hours. At 1929 prices the fuel cost

TABLE XLII

FUEL AND LUBRICANTS USED PER TRACTOR ON THE HOME FARM

(From United States Department of Agriculture Technical Bulletin 384)

	On Drawbar Work			On Belt Work		
	2 Plow Tractor	3 Plow Tractor	General Purpose	2 Plow Tractor	3 Plow Tractor	General Purpose
Hours used per year...	269	256	433	32	41	38
Average crop acreage .	184	226	196	184	216	196
Fuel per year:						
Gasoline, gallons...	104	275	156	17	46	15
Kerosene, gallons...	402	315	607	36	46	48
Fuel oil, gallons....	9	70	..	1	6	..
Total, gallons....	515	660	763	54	98	63
Oil, gallons..........	22	26	31	3	4	3
Grease, pounds.......	12	12	13	1	2	1
Quantity used per hour:						
All fuel, gallons....	1.9	2.6	1.8	1.7	2.4	1.6
Oil, gallons........	.08	.10	.07	.08	.10	.08
Grease, pounds.....	.043	.046	.030	.043	.046	.030

$78.75, as shown in Table XLIII. Oil was $16.93 and other items brought the variable costs to $119.52. Depreciation amounted to $96.76 and interest on investment $26.17. The total cost was $242.45, or 80.4 cents per hour.

The total yearly cost for the three-plow tractors was

$335.26, or $1.129 per hour. General purpose tractors were operated an average of 471 hours per year. This cost $287.66 or 61 cents per hour.

TABLE XLIII

AVERAGE COST OF USING TRACTOR ON THE
HOME FARM, 1929

(From United States Department of Agriculture Technical Bulletin 384)

	2 Plow Tractor	3 Plow Tractor	General Purpose Tractor
Hours used per year................	301	297	471
Acres of crops, average.............	184	226	196
Average costs per year:			
Fuel, @ 13.8 cents per gallon......	$ 78.75	$105.66	$115.01
Oil, @ 68 cents per gallon.........	16.93	20.78	23.31
Grease @ 15 cents per pound......	1.94	2.03	2.10
Chore labor, @ 28½ cents per hour	6.08	6.42	9.45
Repairs and expert labor..........	14.20	26.28	6.93
Farm repair labor @ 28½ cents per hour.......................	1.62	2.35	.91
Total variable cost.............	$119.52	$163.52	$157.71
Depreciation....................	$ 96.76	$133.39	$103.26
Interest........................	26.17	38.35	26.69
Total fixed cost................	$122.93	$171.74	$129.95
Total of all costs[a]..............	242.45	335.26	287.66
Average cost per hour..........	.804	1.129	.610
Average costs at 1931-'32 prices:			
Total cost per year[a]...............	$231.81	$300.35	$246.02
Cost per hour....................	.710	1.011	.523

[a] Not including shelter, taxes, or insurance for tractor or wages for operator.

If 1931-32 prices are used the variable costs are reduced considerably while fixed expenses remain as before. At this price level the cost per hour for the two-plow tractor

would be 71 cents.   For the three-plow it would be $1.011
and for the general purpose tractor 52.3 cents.

The low cost per hour for the general purpose tractor

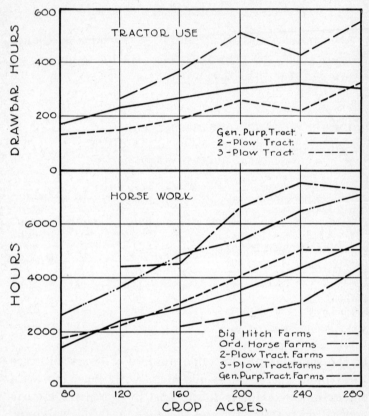

Fig. 50.—Average annual use of horses and tractors on corn belt
farms.   Data from U. S. Department of Agriculture Technical Bulletin 384.

is mostly due to its being used so much during the year.
Fuel and oil consumption is nearly as high as with the
ordinary two-plow tractor, and fixed expenses are slightly

higher.   The effect of spreading the $129.95 of fixed expense over 471 hours instead of 300 hours per year is to lower cost per hour by nearly 16 cents.

Combined Use of Horses and Tractor

Most farms with tractors also use some horses.   Figure 50 shows that the general purpose tractor is used more hours per year than the ordinary or old type on farms

TABLE XLIV

RELATION OF CROP ACREAGE PER FARM TO NUMBER OF HORSES DISPLACED BY TRACTORS

(From Minnesota Bulletin 280)

CROP ACREAGE			WORK HORSES PER FARM			Crop
Group	Average	Number of Farms	At Present	Number Needed Without Tractor	Displaced by Tractor	Acres per Horse Displaced
Under 100..	79	24	4.3	5.3	1.0	79
100-199....	145	108	5.5	7.6	2.1	69
200-299....	245	79	7.2	10.1	2.9	84
300-399....	336	34	8.2	12.6	4.4	76
400-499....	442	18	10.2	16.3	6.1	72
500 and over	772	28	11.7	22.6	10.9	71
All Farms..	268	291	7.1	10.7	3.6	74

of the same size.   The same number of hours with the three-plow tractor represents more work done than with the two-plow.   Horses do the least work where there is a general purpose tractor and the most on farms where big hitches are used.

How many horses will a tractor replace?   Table XLIV shows that, according to a Minnesota study, an average reduction of one horse per farm occurred when a tractor was purchased on farms of less than 100 crop acres.   There was a reduction of 2.1 horses where there were 100 to 199 crop acres. The purchase of a tractor does not permit a farmer to dispose of horses which had done as much work as the tractor can do. On many farms the addition of a tractor means more power than is needed.

What is the most economical combination of power? Table XLV shows the use of horses alone is most economical up to 180 crop acres. Above this point a general purpose tractor with some horses is more economical than horses alone. Above 220 crop acres the two-plow tractor becomes as economical or more so than using only horses. The three-plow tractor is the least economical of the various outfits studied.

Choosing Between Horses and Tractor

With this information, how should a farmer choose between using horses alone, or a smaller number of horses and a tractor? Let us go back to the farmer we used as an example in the last chapter. He raised 157 acres of corn, 91 acres of oats, and 6 acres of alfalfa. He had an old tractor which was about worn out and seven horses. He hired about nine months of labor besides his own and that of his father, who helped with the chores.

Two complete power outfits should be enough. These might either be two teams of five horses each or a tractor and one such team. In either case it would be well to keep an extra horse in case one should be unable to work. On this farm, then, the choice is between eleven horses, or six horses and a tractor. He should be able to get along with one less horse than the seven he now has.

The farmer should use figures from his own records as far as possible in making his choice. His records show that his seven horses used about 210 bushels of corn, 270 bushels of oats, 4 tons of alfalfa, 8 tons of straw, $4\frac{1}{2}$ months of pasturage, and 3 months of stalk pasturage. These feeds could be used by hogs or cattle to return a cash income. At prevailing prices the value of the feed is $395. Miscellaneous expenses amounted to $140, and indirect expenses for depreciation and interest to $56. The total

TABLE XLV

AVERAGE ANNUAL COST PER CROP ACRE OF ALL
POWER USED, 1929. INCLUDING OWNED
AND HIRED POWER, VARIATION
WITH SIZE OF FARM

(From U. S. Department of Agriculture Technical Bulletin 384)

Types of Farm	Two-Plow Tractor	Three-Plow Tractor	General Purpose Tractor	Ordinary Horse Farms
Size Group (Crop Acres)				
Less than 60...........	....	....	....	$8.51
60 to 99..............	$8.87	$9.93	....	6.81
100 to 139............	6.30	7.02	$6.31	5.70
140 to 179............	5.54	6.53	5.16	4.88
180 to 219............	4.91	5.90	4.52	4.86
220 to 259............	4.72	5.36	4.06	4.84
260 to 299............	4.05	4.60	4.59	4.03
300 and over..........	3.95	4.41	3.45	4.14
Average..........	5.13	5.34	4.70	5.32

expense for the horses, not counting chore labor, was $591, or $84 per horse, which is lower than the figures in Table XLI. Of course no charge for labor has been included nor is there allowance for manure credit. These two will probably about offset each other.

Recorded costs on the old tractor will not help much, though. There have been many repairs, while depreciation and interest charges are less than they would be on a new tractor. Such figures as those in Table XLIII will probably be more accurate. If the farmer buys a new tractor it should be of the general-purpose type.

From Table XLIII we find that if chore labor is left out to make the figures comparable to those on his horses, the

Courtesy John Deere Co.

Fig. 51.—A tractor doing light work where horses would be cheaper.

total cost of operating such a tractor for 471 hours would be about $278. He would probably use a new tractor about that much.

Now we can compare costs. If eleven horses were used at a cost of $84 each, the total power cost for his farm would be about $924. Six horses would cost $504 and the tractor $278, a total of $782. In this case there would be an advantage of $142 in favor of the tractor.

Non-Financial Considerations

The farmer's decision should not be based entirely on financial considerations. Will the tractor and horses do equally good work? What is it worth to have a tractor available for belt work, which the horses could not do at all? How much flexibility in the labor program is possible because the tractor can be used longer hours per day than the horses, especially in hot weather? How much of the horse feed could actually be converted into cash by feeding it to other livestock or by direct sale? Finally, is the cash available for buying and operating a tractor?

The size of the farm often determines whether a tractor should be bought or all the work done with horses. Another important question is whether or not the number of horses may actually be reduced. If no reduction is made, the tractor is mostly an added expense. The topography of the land is also important in deciding on the power outfit. In hilly sections, tractors may be unsatisfactory because of side slippage on hills.

The farmer's personal preferences and aptitudes also enter in. Some men prefer to work with horses, others enjoy working with tractors. Under the same set of conditions a tractor might be economical for one man and horses for another.

References

California Bulletin 401: "Cost of Work Horses on California Farms," by R. L. Adams, 1926.

Illinois Bulletin 329: "Organizing the Corn Belt Farm for Profitable Production," by H. C. M. Case, R. H. Wilcox, and H. A. Berg, 1929.

Indiana Bulletin 332: "Relation of Farm Power and Farm Organization in Central Indiana," by O. G. Lloyd and L. G. Hobson, 1929.

Iowa Bulletin 264: "Horses, Tractors, and Farm Equipment,"
by John A. Hopkins, 1929.

Iowa Circular 130: "Feeding and Management of Horses," by
A. B. Caine, 1931.

Minnesota Bulletin 280: "The Farm Tractor in Minnesota," by
A. J. Schwantes and G. A. Pond, 1931.

New York (Cornell) Bulletin 506: "An Economic Study of
Tractors on New York Farms," by C. W. Gilbert, 1930.

South Dakota Circular 6: "Tractor and Horse Power in the
Wheat Area of South Dakota," by C. M. Hampson and
Paul Christopherson, 1932.

U. S. Department of Agriculture, Department Bulletin 1202:
"Tractors and Horses in the Winter Wheat Belt; Okla-
homa, Kansas, Nebraska," by H. R. Tolley and W. R.
Humphries, 1924.

U. S. Department of Agriculture, Technical Bulletin 384:
"Utilization and Cost of Power on Corn Belt Farms," by
L. A. Reynoldson, W. R. Humphries, S. R. Speelman, E. W.
McComas, and W. H. Youngman, 1933.

PART VI

SUMMARY OF THE BUDGET

CHAPTER XVIII

Budgeting for General Expenses

The Problem: What other expenses besides direct outlay on crops and livestock should be planned for in the budget? How can the farmer estimate the amounts of these items?

Elements of Direct and Indirect Expense

Many farmers have made what they thought were conservative plans, only to find their net income smaller than they expected, because they had forgotten to take into account a lot of incidental expenses. These incidental expenses often make up a relatively large part of the total outlay of the farm.

Expenses which apply directly to the planting of a crop or the handling of a livestock enterprise may be called *direct expenses*. Purchases of seed or fertilizer, threshing expenses, purchases of feed, and veterinary bills are clearly chargeable to specific enterprises.

Besides these, there are expenses which apply to groups of enterprises and cannot be charged to any particular one. Wages paid to the hired man, who may work at several different jobs each day, are of this type. Some of the jobs at which he works, such as caring for the horses, may be for the general benefit of the farm and not chargeable to any single crop. Other such expenses are for upkeep and repair of equipment, expenses on truck or farm auto-

271

mobile, and similar items. These items may be called *variable*, or operating expenses. That is, if the farmer should decide to dispose of his livestock and not operate the farm for a year, these expenses would automatically stop.

Courtesy of John Deere Co.

Fig. 52.—Threshing is a good example of a variable expense.

There is another type of expense which applies only indirectly to productive enterprises. These are the *fixed expenses,* such as taxes, rent, interest on borrowed funds, upkeep of permanent improvements, and insurance. These would continue even though the farmer stopped operating the farm. Taxes and interest would have to be paid in order to keep possession of the farm, whether crops were raised or not. It would still be necessary to keep buildings in repair to avoid future heavy losses from deterioration, and to pay fire insurance premiums to avoid possible losses.

Both direct and indirect expenses should be planned for as far in advance as possible. The best time is when the farmer is making up his budget. How can he estimate the amount of each item?

Table XLVI shows what these expenses were on a group of Iowa farms in 1929. On these farms the average total income was $6,858. Out of this an average of $3,262 was spent. Purchase of feeds, which amounted to $809, was the largest item. Direct expenses on crops and livestock each took slightly over $100. Repairs to equipment cost $249 and expenses of the automobile chargeable to the farm business took $107. Wages to hired labor amounted to a little over $400.

Among the fixed expenses, rent and interest on borrowed funds each required between $400 and $500. Taxes took nearly $300, and upkeep of permanent improvements over $100. Total direct operating expenses were $1,051. Indirect expenses came to $849, and fixed expenses to $1,362.

Budgeting for Labor

The expense for hired labor can usually be estimated fairly accurately on a farm which is already being operated. If accounts have been kept, the farmer needs only to turn to the records of the preceding year to find a basis for his estimate. If there are no records, an estimate may be made from memory. Memory, however, is likely to prove imperfect, and some items, such as odd days' labor hired during busy seasons, are apt to be forgotten.

If the farmer is moving onto a new farm, or is changing

his system, he will have to use other methods in making his estimate.   He must first consider labor requirements of the crop and livestock enterprises at the various sea-

TABLE XLVI

ELEMENTS OF EXPENSE ON 632 IOWA FARMS—1929

GROSS INCOME... $6858

EXPENSES:

Operating Expenses:

Direct Operating Expenses:

Feeds bought.................................	$ 809
Crop expense.................................	139
Livestock expense............................	103
Total Direct Expense.............................	$1051

Indirect Operating Expense:

Equipment repairs.............................	$ 249
Auto (farm share).............................	107
Tractor and truck.............................	34
Labor hired..................................	410
Misc. operating expense.......................	49
Total Indirect Operating Expense....................	$ 849

Fixed Expenses:

Rent...	$ 481
Taxes..	290
Interest paid.................................	447
Insurance....................................	32
Upkeep—Permanent improvements................	112
Total Fixed Expense..............................	$1362

Total Expense.....................................	3262
DEPRECIATION AND DECREASE IN ASSETS......................	833
NET INCOME.......................................	2763

sons.   Then he must figure how much labor he will have to hire and estimate the wages he will have to pay.   Only hired labor should, of course, be included in the budget. (The work of the farmer and his family involves no cash outlay. He gets for his labor whatever he is able to make, and this comes to him as part of the net income.)

Expenses on equipment. Unless the farmer has had some experience both with farming and with keeping records, he will probably have to be satisfied with a rough estimate of probable costs of repairs and upkeep of equipment. This expense varies widely from year to year. Accidents or misfortunes may make it high in some years, while in others such expenses may be trivial.

Expenses on auto. Allowance for such use of the auto as may reasonably be charged to the farm business should be included in the budget. This will not include all auto expenses, since it is also used for personal affairs. The latter belong to the household or personal expenses.

The past years' records are a great help, but even without records it should be possible to estimate rather closely. Making a complete list of all types of expense helps to avoid omissions. Gas, oil, insurance, tires, repairs, and license should all be listed. After the estimate of total auto expense has been made, the next step is to divide it between farm and personal use. This may not be easy to do, since many trips combine business and personal errands.

Budgeting for fixed expenses. Fixed expenses are usually easier to anticipate than operating expenses. On a rented farm, the rent is decided in advance and will take either a fixed amount of money or a fixed portion of the crops.

If the farmer owns the land, there will be expenses for taxes and possibly for interest. Most of the interest will be on funds already borrowed, and therefore easy to figure. The only doubtful element will be the possible need for borrowing within the year.   Taxes can usually be forecast within a few dollars.

Upkeep of buildings and other permanent improvements is rather difficult to foresee.   Of course, one can usually see the deterioration of buildings and fences developing for some time before it is necessary to make re-

Courtesy King Ventilating Co.

Fig 53.—A large and expensive barn is convenient and comfortable for livestock but means a heavy interest and depreciation load for many years.

pairs.   Still fences may be washed away by a flood or the roof of a building may be torn off by a storm, and it is not possible to make allowances for such accidents in advance.

With the upkeep of buildings and equipment it is possible to control to a certain degree the amount of repairs made in a given year.   When funds are low, some repairs can be postponed for months or even years. Sometimes this may even be a genuine economy. When hard pressed, we can often get along without things which we usually consider very important. This is of course by no means always true. Delay often leads to greater expense. If a leak in a roof is not mended, it is likely to rot the rafters or damage the contents of the building. A neglected hole in the barn floor may cause a horse to break a leg. A very important exercise of judgment is involved, in times of financial stress, in deciding which repairs can be put off and which should not be.

Summarizing the Budget

Now that estimates of income and of expense have been made, we are ready to bring these figures together into a summary form. This is illustrated in Form E. This form also shows the sources from which the summary data are obtained. On the receipts side of the statement, the crop sales are found and transferred from the Crop Budget (Form A, page 133). The livestock sales are to be found in Form D, page 214. Estimates of livestock products to be used in the house will be found in the same place. Values of vegetables, fuel, and such items will have to be estimated now, as well as any important source of income not previously provided for.

On the expense side of the summary the figures dealing with direct expenses on crops will be totalled in the crop budget. Those for expenses on livestock and feeds will be obtained from the budget of livestock requirements (Form C, page 208). Other items, indicated by asterisks, will have to be estimated now for the first time and entered in this form. There should be no difficulty in drawing up this summary as far as the essential figures are concerned.   The fixed expenses and the operating expenses have been computed in connection with earlier tables.

SUMMARY OF EXPECTED RECEIPTS AND EXPENSES

EXPECTED RECEIPTS		EXPECTED EXPENSES	
Livestock: (from Form D, page 214)		*Direct Operating Expenses:*	
Cattle................	$ 592.00	Feed to be bought....	$ 180.00
Butterfat............	540.00	Livestock expense.....	35.00
Hogs.................	1526.00	(Form C, page 208)	
Poultry products......	281.00	Crop expense.........	165.00
Total livestock		(Form A, page 133)	
receipts..........	$2939.00	Total direct oper.	
		expense..........	$ 380.00
Crops: (from Form A, page 133)		*Indirect Operating Expenses:*	
Corn.................	....	Equipment upkeep*...	$ 80.00
....	....	Auto (farm share)*....	120.00
....	....	Labor to be hired*....	75.00
Total crop sales.....	....	Total indirect oper.	
		expenses........	$275.00
Farm Products to Household:		*Fixed Expenses:*	
Livestock products		Rent*...............	....
(Form D).........	$ 147.00	Taxes*..............	$ 200.00
Vegetables, fuel, etc.*.	100.00	Interest*............	60.00
Total to household..	$ 247.00	Insurance*..........	30.00
		Improvements, upkeep*	25.00
		Total fixed expense..	$ 315.00
		Total Expenditures.....	$ 970.00
Total Expected Income..	$3186.00	Total Expected Net	
		Income..............	$2216.00

* Denotes estimates entered for the first time on this form.

Computing the net income. After the various elements of income and expense are all entered in the budget summary, the next step is to add the different columns to obtain the total expected income and expenditure.   In this illustration these amount to $3,186 and $970 respectively.

How much of the receipts will be left after paying the expenses? This will be the expected net income. It is obtained by subtracting the total expenditures from the total income. In this case it should be $2,216 if plans all work out as expected.

Just what does this figure mean? It means that according to our plans the farmer should have $2,216 from the farm during the year to pay him for his labor, for the use of his land and capital, and for his trouble and responsibility in managing the farm. This is the sum that should be available either for family living or for new investments, or for both.

Choosing Between Alternative Budgets

Does this particular budget represent the best that this farmer could do with his farm? We are not sure that it does. It represents the probable returns if he follows the plan outlined, but there may be a better plan. Usually more than one of several possible plans should be considered.

One alternative might be to feed the bulk of the corn to steers instead of hogs. Then, as already suggested, he would compare the net income from a steer-feeding organization with the net income from a hog-producing organization. This could then be done by drawing up a second livestock budget based on the same crop plan. This budget for the steer feeding organization should be worked out completely on Forms C and D, and the summary figures brought together on Form E along with the essential figures from the crop production budget. The net income figure could then be obtained and compared with the prospective net income from the hog-producing organization, as the principal basis for a choice between the two plans.

The benefits from making a budget or plan for the coming year are many and diverse. The primary purpose is to help in working out the most profitable organization of the farm. This is more than merely choosing between the two or three different plans. Having a definite plan of operation results in more efficient management. Budgeting helps the farmer to discover, in advance, elements of expense which do not bring in a satisfactory return. Careful planning during hard times often leads to changing methods or habits of spending which would cause serious loss before the end of the year. It is very worthwhile to discover leaks in the farm business, but it is even better to stop the leak before losses begin.

References

Hopkins, John A., *Farm Records,* Collegiate Press, Ames, Iowa, 1936, Chapter II.

U. S. Department of Agriculture, Farmers Bulletin 1564: "Farm Budgeting," by J. B. Hutson, 1928.

CHAPTER XIX

Records to Check up on Farm Performance

> **The Problem:** After the farm is organized, how is the farmer to know whether or not he is keeping up to his plans? To what extent does this require the use of accounts or records? How can necessary records be kept with the least trouble?

Does a Farmer Need to Keep Records?

After a farmer has planned the organization of his farm he needs to keep a record of his progress from month to month and from year to year. From these he should be able to tell when he departs from his plan or budget in time to correct the error and avoid losses.

If he has had no experience with farm accounts, he may expect them to involve a great deal of work and trouble. He will probably wonder if he should keep records after all. How would he go about setting them up? How much time and trouble would they require? What benefits would they bring?

It is true that only a small percentage of farmers keep any sort of systematic records. Do they lose anything by the lack of records? Would they get along better if they had them? The person who does not have records cannot really tell whether he is making any progress in his business or not. The amount of money he has in the bank will not tell him. His bank account may have

changed because he has incurred new debts during the
year or has paid off old ones.   He may have either larger
or smaller inventories of grain and livestock on hand.
His memory will hardly give a correct comparison between the total of all these present items and those of a
year ago.   It is even less likely that he can make any accurate comparison with the corresponding figures of two
or three years before.

A well-planned set of records will tell the condition of
the business at inventory dates.   They also enable the
farmer to compare its condition at previous inventory
dates.   Once a fact is recorded, it remains as clear and
definite after ten years as after ten days.

Such records may be useful in unexpected ways.   The
farmer should of course be able to tell from the accounts
what the receipts and expenses were for each branch of
the business.   As he examines his crop and livestock records, he can tell just how well each of his enterprises is
doing and compare this year's performance with that of
previous years.

If a farmer can join a coöperative farm record group he
can compare his results with those of his neighbors.   If
there is no such group in his neighborhood, he can compare his results with those from the farm management
studies carried on at the agricultural experiment station
of his own or a neighboring state.   These comparisons
are always interesting and sometimes startling.   A farmer who had thought himself an efficient hog raiser may
discover that his hogs have been using much more than
the standard amount of feed per hundred pounds of gain,
and that the farm profit may have actually been coming
from some enterprise that he had not considered especially strong.   Or he may find that the steer feeding in

which he had taken pride was really a source of loss while his hogs were yielding a good return.

Do check stubs constitute a set of records?   When the subject of keeping accounts is mentioned, the farmer often says, "Yes, I have a record of everything; I pay all my bills with checks."   What sort of record does he have? After several months have passed it is often impossible to tell what had been the purpose of a check made out to a store.   The check may have covered several items which cannot be separated later.   Besides, many small items were probably paid for in cash without having a check to show for them.   Does the farmer ever summarize the check stubs to find out how much his feed purchases amounted to?   How much the upkeep of his equipment cost?   The operation of his auto?   If asked these questions the farmer will probably reply, "No, but I could if I just went through the cancelled checks and sorted them out."   If the record is incomplete or the nature of the purchase is not entered on the check stub, it would be impossible to make a summary for the farm or for any section of it.

Even if the farmer has kept all the checks with which he paid his bills, what will he do about the receipts of the business?   Will he be able to locate records of all his sales, statements from commission men, records of cream checks and so on?   Some items, such as eggs or poultry, are often sold for cash without a record ever having been made of the transaction.

The farmer who "keeps his checks" will probably agree by now that it is a good habit to do so, but that they do not provide a complete financial record.   The only satisfactory set of records is one that has been planned with that particular business in mind, so that the entire business will be covered. Such records should be drawn up to lead directly, without unnecessary effort, to the specific information that the farmer will need at the end of each month or year.

Those farmers whose incomes are large enough to come under Federal or state income tax laws find financial records an actual necessity. Another need for records of farm production and sales arose when farmers went to apply for hog, corn, wheat, or cotton quotas under the Agricultural Adjustment Act. Farmers with well-kept records found it much easier to obtain their proper quotas.

Kinds of Farm Records

What kind of records should a farmer keep? Such a general question cannot really be answered, because the records should be planned to fit the individual farm.

Nevertheless, the basic methods of accounting remain pretty much the same, no matter what type of farm they are applied to. In most states the Agricultural Extension Services have developed accounting forms suitable to types of farms found in their particular states. Commercial accounting forms are also available in the form of the usual journals, ledgers, and cash books. The problem of obtaining suitable forms is easier than combining the various types of form that will best suit the needs of the specific farmer.

The system finally adopted will depend on how complete an analysis of his business the farmer wants to make. There are four principal stages in recording and analyzing the business. The first consists of an annual comparison of the condition of the business. The second includes these comparisons but adds records of receipts and expenses. In the third there is added a set of statistical records of crop yields, livestock production, and perhaps feed or labor utilization. The fourth brings together the three sets of data as they are applied to each individual enterprise and makes it possible to analyze each one separately.

Photo J. C. Allen and Sons.

Fig. 54.—Time spent on farm records brings a good return.

Inventories Do Not Measure Success

Inventories have already been discussed. In order to get a clear cut picture of the condition of the business it is necessary to take an inventory of all assets and liabilities. For the farmer who wants to spend the least possible time on his records and still be able to make definite comparisons in the size and condition of his business at various intervals, probably yearly, a series of inventories will serve the purpose.

FORM F

RECEIPTS

MONTH.......... YEAR..........

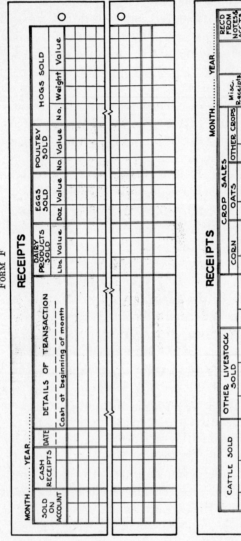

RECEIPTS

MONTH.......... YEAR..........

286

These inventories, however, are of only limited use. Suppose that this year's inventory shows the net worth to be $500 less than a year ago. Such a decrease is important, but the inventory does not tell why the shrinkage occurred, or if the business has been poorly managed. The farm may have been well operated except for one project, which caused a loss. The inventory cannot tell which was the losing enterprise. The business may have made a net income of $1,000, but the farmer's living amounted to $1,500. The inventories show the condition of the business at specified dates, but do not tell what happened between inventory dates. For example, pigs farrowed in March and sold before the end of the year would not appear in either the opening or the closing inventory.

Financial Records to Supplement the Inventories

In order to fill some of the gaps between inventories, a set of financial records is needed. What do the total receipts amount to during the year? How much do the year's cream checks amount to? How much is taken in from the poultry enterprise? How important are the various minor enterprises? Should some of them be made into major enterprises? Such information can be had only by recording all farm receipts as they occur. Memory cannot be depended upon, for by the end of the year many small items are forgotten.

Entering receipts. An accounting form developed by one of the state agricultural extension services will show the type of information that such a set of accounts will yield. Form F shows a loose-leaf financial record developed by the Iowa Agricultural Extension Service. After each sale the description of the transaction is entered in

Form G

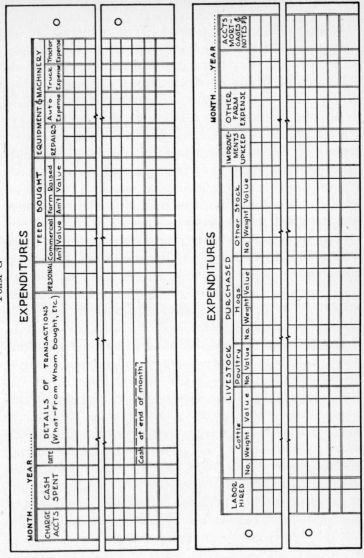

288

the explanation space on the left hand page and the amount of the sale is entered in the indicated column. It is important to record the amount of produce sold. This means the number of pounds of hogs or cattle as well as the number of animals. The number of dozens of eggs, pounds of butterfat, bushels of grain, and such items should be entered at the same time as the amount of money. Very little additional work is required to make this record complete, and it will be very valuable at the end of the year in figuring up butterfat production per cow, egg production per hen, pounds of pork produced per litter, and other rates of production.

The year's summary of receipts is very easily made with this form of record. At the end of each month the columns of receipts are added and the totals carried forward to a summary form on which corresponding columns appear. Here monthly figures can be added to obtain quarterly and yearly totals.

Expenditures. Expenditures are recorded and summarized in about the same manner as the receipts. Form G shows the column headings used in the Iowa form. As with receipts, the date, description of transaction, and quantity of goods bought are entered as well as the amount of money paid out. Expenses, like receipts, are added up once a month and posted to the summary sheet. Usually there will be more entries in the expenditures than in the receipts. Most farms make rather few sales per enterprise, often for large amounts as when a wheat crop or a load of hogs is sold. Expenses are more numerous and usually smaller in amount.

The Income Statement

After the year's financial records are completed, the

total of each type of cash receipt is carried from the summary sheet, just described, to the receipts side of the Income Statement. This statement is drawn up in the same form as the Budget Summary. There are other kinds of income besides cash receipts. Any unrealized income in the form of increased inventories is entered in this statement in order to find the total income for the farm. The value of farm produce used by the family is also entered.

On the other side of the statement is entered the various expense totals and the depreciation on equipment and buildings. Also any decreases in inventories of crops or livestock are recorded here in order to find the total business debits (i.e., expenses, depreciation, and the like). The difference between the total receipts and the total debits constitutes the net income of the farm for the year.

The subtotals of income show the relative importance of various productive enterprises. On the other side the subtotals of expense tell definitely how much outlay was used for each in keeping the farm in operation. The Income Statement supplements the Net Worth Statement. The net worth statement shows the condition of the business at the beginning of the year. There is a similar net worth statement at the end of the year. The income statement completes the story by telling what happened between inventory dates. The one statement gives a picture of the financial structure of the business, the other gives its financial history.

We will return to the financial accounts in a later chapter, when we take up the analysis of the business. In the meantime the student would find it very helpful if he began to keep a current financial record of his father's farm or some other farm with which he is acquainted so that, later on, he will be able to work with definite data in which he is interested.

With the financial records completed and the income statement before him, the farmer is in a position to know the net income or the profit on the farm business. Now, if his inventories show that the net worth is $500 less than the year before, he can tell whether the loss came from heavy personal expenditures or from unsatisfactory management of the business.

Can a farmer find from his income statement which particular enterprise is to blame for a small net income? This information is still lacking, although he knows what was the direct income from each source. In the farm business each enterprise depends on others in many ways. Expenses are incurred in one enterprise, such as hay or corn, and the receipts come from another, cattle or hogs which used the feed. Therefore, direct expenses and direct income give no indication of the success of an enterprise.

Records of Production and Physical Performance

Records of physical performance in farm operation should be kept to provide information on operating efficiency. These will help in evaluating the different enterprises.

The farmer will probably think first of a record of crop yields. This is simple and requires little work to keep, since it is only necessary to enter the acreages and yields of each crop once a year. If the record is expanded to include soil treatment, it will be still more helpful in guiding the farm policy.

A feed record. A record of feed consumption by the various livestock projects furnishes other very useful in-

formation. One of the most satisfactory records of feed
consumption is obtained from estimates of the amounts of
feeds used daily by each livestock enterprise. The estimates are made at the beginning of the month or whenever a change is made in the rations. They should be
checked occasionally by weighing and measuring. Of
course these estimates do not give an exact record, but the
error is seldom over five or ten per cent. This is sufficiently accurate to furnish a useful check on the farmer's
feeding efficiency. Such a record should not require more
than a half hour's work per month. Since feed is a large
part of the total cost in livestock production, it is difficult
to manage livestock projects intelligently without such a
record.

Record of livestock production. Rates of gain on fattening animals are as important as the amounts of feed
used in obtaining them. Such information can easily be
had by recording weights of livestock bought or sold, dates
of purchase or sale, and dates when put on feed. The rate
of gain per day is found by dividing the total gain by the
number of days the animals were on feed.

The number of pounds of butterfat or pounds of milk
produced per cow can be computed if sales are recorded
each time a cream or milk check is received and an estimate added each month or year of the amount used by
the household. The number of eggs laid per hen can be
found if the number of dozens of eggs as well as the money
received is recorded when eggs are sold. To get a complete record of egg production, this must be supplemented
by an estimate of the number used by the family as well
as the number used for hatching.

Most of the data necessary for the record of livestock
production can be obtained along with the financial record

with a little extra effort in recording quantities of purchases or sales as well as the amounts of money.

A labor record. Labor records are another kind of statistical information kept on some farms. But making a record of the number of hours spent on each job means writing down this information at the end of each day before it is forgotten. This is apt to be a laborious task and seldom worth the effort it takes. While the labor record will usually show some places where unproductive labor could be cut out, it does not indicate the most efficient method of doing a job, because there is seldom anything to compare it with. The farmer is not apt to be using two or three different sizes of machines, for example, at the same time.

Records of crop production and soil treatment, the feed record, and the livestock production records are sure to be useful and can be kept without much effort. By studying the data furnished by these records, the farmer can get a pretty accurate idea of the efficiency of his different enterprises. *The first step toward improvement is to find out where the weaknesses are and what they are.*

Enterprise Analysis

After the year's records have been completed, it is important that a careful analysis be made of the separate enterprises. This means bringing together for each enterprise the inventories, accounts of purchases and sales, information about the methods used, and livestock production and feed records.

Each enterprise will require a slightly different form of analysis. Returns will probably be considered first, including both sales and changes in values of inventories. Production figures should be studied. With crops this will be the yields per acre. For livestock there will be the rates of gains per day, the milk per cow, eggs per hen, and so on. Next, the input of seed, fertilizer, and feed should be summarized and compared to amounts produced. Both these sets of figures should be compared with standards obtained from experiment station figures or average results obtained by good farmers.

The methods used in carrying on the enterprise should be carefully examined. Are the varieties of crops the best that can be raised on that particular farm? Have diseases and insect pests been controlled? Are the methods of preparing the seedbed and cultivating the crop the best that can be used there?

Have the livestock been raised under sanitary conditions? Can anything else be done to prevent disease? Could more economical or more efficient rations be worked out? Methods of feeding, length of feeding period, and marketing practices should all be studied to see if mistakes are being made or if more economical methods are possible.

Enterprise analysis should be tied in with the budget. Such a study of records will usually uncover most of the serious causes for loss. Besides the study of individual enterprises it will of course be necessary to go over the entire budget or farm plan, to make sure that the enterprises are of a kind and size that are suited to the whole farm.

Farm Cost Accounts

Cost accounting is another method that might be used to evaluate the results of the different enterprises. By this method, figures showing the total cost per unit of product and profit from each enterprise would be computed. At first glance this seems to have much to recommend it, but further study shows up its undesirable features.

In order to compute the cost per unit of corn, for example, it is necessary to assign values to all the elements of production that we are using in raising that crop. This means that the labor, horse labor, use of equipment, seed, manure, use of buildings, and so on, must all have definite valuations placed on them. In most cases this can be done in only an arbitrary manner. Even in the case of labor, decisions must be made that are arbitrary and therefore open to error. For example, the hired man is hired by the month. If corn were the only crop grown, all his wages would be chargeable to corn. But corn does not need labor continuously, and there are times when the hired man can work at something else without adding to the labor bill.

The slack time job is likely to bring less income per hour than the work on corn. How much should be charged to corn and how much to the other work? Charging both at the same rate is hardly satisfactory, since the fill-in job might not be done at all if labor had to be hired especially for it. On the other hand, the labor bill would be just as great if there were no rainy-day jobs to fill in.

The same trouble occurs with the other elements of expense. Horses are needed to plow corn, but at other times they can be doing something else with little added expense. Old buildings often continue to be used for purposes which may bring in only small returns, but since they are already there, anything which can be got from them is so much net gain. What should be charged for them?

There are so many arbitrary figures in the "costs" on an

individual enterprise that they have little meaning. A farmer often computes a "cost" figure which shows that he is losing money by raising oats, for example, and yet he realizes that the crop is a necessary part of his cropping system, as a nurse crop for legumes in the rotation. If he stopped raising the crop he would lose more than if he continued to plant it. When cost accounts show such results we know they are unsound.

We may conclude that the cost accounts seldom show satisfactory results that could not have been obtained more easily by other methods. Often they are seriously misleading. Much more information can be obtained from financial records and the study of enterprise efficiency than from cost accounts, and the information is in a more usable form.

Coöperative Farm Accounting Associations

The coöperative farm accounting association is a recent development. From it the farmer can get valuable assistance in understanding and applying information from his records. The coöperative association is generally composed of a hundred or more farm record keepers. It employs a trained farm management worker who helps the members to work out their management problems. Much depends on the ability of this "route" man. If he is well trained and alert, he can add very materially to the farmers' incomes.

Under this method each farmer keeps his own record and the field man checks it over to make sure it is complete and correct. He should visit each farm once every two or three months. During this visit he talks over the farmer's problems with him and points out weaknesses which should be strengthened or opportunities that are being neglected. Both crop and livestock methods should be talked over, and particularly those jobs which are to be done in the weeks just ahead.

The route man is able to keep a list of improved varieties of seeds and of breeding animals which can be obtained from other members of the association. He can also help the farmer to apply outlook information to his own situation. His observations and opinions are often very valuable, since he is outside the routine work of the farm and is able to compare performance of the various farms in the group.

At the end of the year the route man takes charge of the process of summarizing the records and of working out helpful comparisons between groups of farms which have used various methods or that represent different types of organization.

References

Currier, Lennes, and Merrill, *Farm Accounting*, Macmillan, New York, 1924.

Hopkins, John A., *Farm Records*, Collegiate Press, Ames, Iowa, 1936.

McMurray and McNall, *Farm Accounting*, A. W. Shaw, Chicago, 1926.

Scovill, Hiram T., *Farm Accounting*, Appleton, New York, 1920.

Part VII

CURRENT OPERATION OF THE FARM

CHAPTER XX

Making Efficient Use of Labor

The Problem: How can the farmer make the best use of his own and of his hired labor? How should he plan his work program from day to day? How can he decide when it is profitable to hire labor, and how should he go about selecting a hired man?

Labor a Limiting Factor in Farm Operation

We sometimes hear a farmer say that he would like to expand his operations by renting more land, milking more cows, or feeding more cattle or hogs, but that he is afraid he would not be able to get the needed help. If he did find a hired man, he says, the man would probably be undependable.

Labor is the limiting factor in many farm operations. The farmer may not hesitate to employ more capital in the form of more machinery or livestock, but the problem of looking after another hired man makes him stop and think. He never feels able to handle a group of men such as he sees working on a road construction gang or in a factory.

Why is labor difficult or unprofitable to use in large quantities on a farm? There are two main reasons. First, labor needs continuous supervision to be effective. If a large number of laborers are to be used, they must be concentrated in a small area for economical supervision. In a factory a large force is assembled in a single room under the watchful eye of the foremen. A good foreman is able to get the maximum amount of work from a large number of men.

Conditions of work on a farm are very different. The hired man is completely out of the farmer's sight most of the time. Two hired men may be working at opposite sides of the farm. With most farm operations it is not possible to keep men working together in a gang. Such work as berry picking or sugar beet harvesting is of course an exception, but this kind of work does not require high-grade labor. Much of it is done by groups of women and children or by families working together.

The seasonal nature of farm tasks also makes it difficult to handle labor efficiently. In a factory it is usually possible to train each worker to do some relatively simple task and then have him continue at it month after month. Only a few farm operations continue for more than two weeks. Most of the more important jobs depend on clear weather. If it rains during the crop-growing season the farmer must stop field work and look for an indoor job. Even in clear weather there are several different kinds of work to be done in the course of the day, such as milking, feeding livestock, then perhaps raking, hauling, stacking or mowing hay, and more chores in the evening. After harvest is over the new helper must be taught to fix fences, haul manure, and so on.

Under the conditions of the ordinary farm, the factor limiting the size of the business is quite generally the number of laborers the farmer can supervise closely and keep efficiently employed under the changing demands of farm operation.

Is the Farm Labor Supply Insufficient?

Is there a sufficient supply of farm help? The farmer often feels that if more labor were available he could expand his business or do his work more thoroughly.   As it is, he must be very careful to limit his work to the most essential jobs, although he would like to keep buildings and fences in better repair and tend the farmstead more carefully.   Where there is relatively little help some of these things must be neglected.   Which should be done carefully and which may be neglected or postponed? This is entirely from the business viewpoint.   From a social viewpoint, it is sometimes preferable to neglect farm work to take a vacation, to beautify the farmstead or make the house more comfortable.

Wages and prices determine the amount of labor to hire.   Evidently there is not enough farm labor to do all the things a farmer might like to have done.   But is there a lack of labor to do all the things that would be *profitable?*   By "profitable" we mean those farm operations which promise a return greater than the wages and other expenses incurred.   Profit depends partly on the prices at which various farm products are sold and partly on the prevailing wages for farm labor.   If wages are $2 per day it is profitable to raise certain crops and do certain jobs.   If wages rise to $3 per day it might be unprofitable to do some of the things which would have paid at $2 a day, provided prices of products have not also changed in the meantime.   The farmer should be concerned not about whether there is a scarcity of labor, but about *which jobs should be done and which left undone at prevailing farm prices and wage levels.*

On most farms the operator himself does most of the work, hiring extra labor only during the peak seasons. He does not hire one or more men the year round because he sees no way to keep extra help profitably employed during the slack seasons.

Making the Most Profitable Use of Labor

The typical corn belt farmer has, besides his own labor, the equivalent of four or five months of family labor and hired labor averaging about three or four months during the year. In order to get the largest returns from this

Fig. 55.—Work like this takes priority over all else.

labor he should, first, select those enterprises that promise to make the best use of his resources. This we have already discussed in earlier chapters. Second, he should plan and equip his farm to use labor most efficiently.

Seeing that work is done well and at the right time also helps to get the most from labor. Two or three days' delay in cultivating corn when weeds are beginning to grow, or a little delay in harvest may cost more than the entire wage bill.   Hurrying through some jobs may save a little time, but if it means covering up many corn hills or over-looking ears during husking, it will be poor economy.

Planning the work so that the fullest possible use is made of every available hour of labor is important.   Work that is urgent should be done without delay, while work than can be postponed should be saved for slack seasons. There should be profitable work for rainy days.   During the crop season the full day should be utilized, and utilized *effectively*.   Some farmers get to the field late in the morning or take a long noon hour, while others put in a long day but putter around so much they get little done.

Seasonal Demands for Labor and the Supply

Demands for labor on most types of farms are very sea-sonal.   During the planting and harvest seasons there is generally a serious need for extra labor.   Can labor be hired for the peak season, or is it necessary to hire men for the entire year in order to have them when needed?   The answer depends on the type of farm and its location. Nearby cities or towns may furnish seasonal labor.   For some kinds of seasonal labor, such as truck farming or sugar-beet growing, there are regular migrations of the kind of labor that can be used economically for these jobs.

Seasonal or migratory labor is generally unskilled. For exacting and skilled work a better grade of laborer must be hired.   These require higher wages in order to get them away from other skilled occupations or from other farmers who want high-grade labor.   In order to have good workers when they are needed, it is usually ne-cessary to employ them all year.   When farmers or other employers complain of the poor quality of seasonal labor, they should realize that good men deserve and can find year-round employment elsewhere.

The amount of field work that can be done during the day varies of course with the length of day during the different seasons. Only about eight hours per day are available during the winter for outside work, while it is possible to work eleven or twelve during the summer. The general tendency is to reduce length of the working day, but the farms have lagged behind the cities in this respect. On the farm there is much to gain by working longer hours in the summer, while this is seldom true in the cities. The variation in hours between harvest and slack seasons on the farm permits perhaps a third more work per man when it is needed for short periods. This added flexibility is very important in the labor plans.

Fitting the Worker to the Type of Work

The requirements of different farm jobs vary as much as the workers available to do them. Very little training or ability is needed to weed truck crops or pick berries, but a highly trained and capable man is needed to operate a combine or mechanical corn picker.

Employing high-grade and experienced men for the more exacting work is sure to be most economical in the long run. An untrained or careless man in half an hour may smash a piece of machinery that costs more than his year's wages. If he is operating a mechanical corn picker, by driving carelessly and neglecting to adjust the snapping rollers, he may shell and knock off 20 or 30 bushels more a day than the skilled operator.

For unskilled work, however, it is a waste of money to hire a high-grade man. A farmer often hires a relatively unskilled man to do the less exacting routine work, while he himself takes charge of the jobs that require skill and judgment.

There are many small routine jobs on a farm that require some judgment and responsibility but no great physical strength. This kind of work is often done by the farmer's wife or sons. The wife usually regards the poultry enterprise as her particular responsibility. The wife and boys often help with milking and livestock feeding. During the busy season, members of the family sometimes do light field work, such as raking. When we consider the opportunities for using labor from members of the family, the possibilities of working longer hours during the rush seasons, and the fact that cheap labor can often be used, we see that there is really a great deal of flexibility in the farm labor supply. If the farmer had to hire only skilled labor for a fixed number of hours each day during the year, his labor bill would be very greatly increased.

Selecting the Hired Man

The problem of selecting the right man to work on a particular farm is one that deserves serious thought and effort on the part of the farmer. Too often the farmer hires the first man who comes along and asks for the job. A dishonest or incapable man may easily cost more than the higher wage of a good man.

On most farms that employ only one or two men the hired help is usually taken into the home, and the farmer's wife and children are thrown into contact with them. Not only is the wrong kind of hired man unpleasant to associate with, but he may have a bad influence upon the children.

In strictly rural districts where there are many young men who hope themselves to become farmers, it is often possible to employ a neighbor's son with whom the farmer is already well acquainted. Such an arrangement will probably give the most satisfactory quality as well as amount of work. The personal relationships are most likely to be agreeable, and the neighbor's son will probably take the greatest interest in his work.

If neighborhood help is not available, the next best arrangement is usually to employ from a nearby rural town a man whose experience and personal history can be investigated before he is hired. If this, too, fails the farmer must resort to an employment agency or pick up a worker who happens along.

When it is necessary to hire a complete stranger, specific information about his qualifications will probably be incomplete. Nevertheless, it is worth while to try to find out as much as possible about him before he is hired. The farmer should get as much information as possible from him, by friendly conversation, about his experience, his industry, his intelligence, his health and strength, and his honesty.

He should be questioned about where he has been working, how long he stayed at his last place, and why he left. How much experience has he had with the particular kind of work he will be asked to do? What are his particular interests and aims? Does he want a permanent place or just a job for a few weeks, until the impulse to move on strikes him? Does he have any family ties? Is he consciously trying to improve himself? A few minutes of well-directed conversation will generally bring the man's outstanding characteristics to light. If he is unwilling to give references or seems afraid of having to work overtime or do some disagreeable task, the farmer had better look further for a helper.

After the man is employed, the problem of his relationship with his employer is very important. The farmer will need to use tact and firmness in directing the man in his work. At the same time he must be absolutely fair in dealing with him and able to sympathize with his problems. In no other way can he keep the man's respect and maintain his interest in the work. The relation between employer and employed is a *voluntary* one. No one can be forced or coerced into working, and if he does his best it is only because he *wants* to.

Planning the Labor Schedule

The farmer must plan to keep himself and his helpers busy continuously if he is to get the greatest returns from his farm and his labor bill. He must look ahead so he will always have some remunerative work available. He must decide constantly which jobs should be done first and which may be postponed. This problem changes daily, but nevertheless it will help to have a classification of farm work according to its urgency and the season or kind of weather in which it can be done.

Field work. Field work on crops should come first and must be done in clear weather with moderately dry soil. Spring plowing, preparing the seedbed, and planting the crops must be done at just the right time to be most effective. This is also true of cultivation of crops, cutting and putting up hay, harvesting small grains, threshing from the shock, using a combine, and silo filling. If any of these jobs are delayed, the size or quality of the crop may be seriously affected. Other work should be planned so it will not interfere with these jobs.

Outside work that can be delayed. Some other farm jobs which also require clear weather can be shifted about within certain time limits. These include such tasks as hauling manure, building fences, fall plowing, threshing grain from stacks, husking corn, ditching and tiling, cutting and hauling wood, and outside repairs to buildings. Fall plowing, ditching, and fencing must be done before the ground freezes. Wood cutting, corn husking, manure

Fig. 56.—Building fence is work for clear weather but slack seasons.

hauling, and brush cutting can be done after freezing but not after a deep snow.

Work for winter. Work which can be done at any season of the year is usually saved for winter, when outside work cannot be done for any length of time. This includes such jobs as overhauling machinery, repairing or oiling harness, sharpening tools, mixing feeds or fertilizers, cleaning seed, testing corn or other seeds, and doing indoor repair work on buildings.

Work for rainy days.   During the crop growing season, outdoor work may be interrupted by rain.   In order that no time will be wasted, indoor work, such as repairing machinery, sharpening mower sickles, and oiling machinery and harness, should be kept in mind.   First attention on rainy days should be given to jobs which will speed

Courtesy International Harvester Co.

Fig. 57.—Manure hauling is a job for the slack seasons.

up the work on crops in the near future.   After all work of this kind has been taken care of, other indoor tasks, such as mixing feed or fertilizer, grinding feed, and cleaning the barn or shop, should be done.

The farmer who wants to use his labor most efficiently should consider alternative jobs before he starts work on any but the most urgent operations.   When these most important jobs are interrupted by rain or otherwise, it is sometimes hard to think of the next most important job. Carrying around a small notebook in which to jot down memoranda of jobs that need to be done on the next rainy day is a valuable habit. The farmer's problem is more than merely keeping his labor busy. Each day should be done the job that will yield the greatest possible return that day.

References

Holmes, C. L., *Economics of Farm Organization and Management*, Heath, Boston, 1928, Chapter XXI.

Overton, M. H., and Robertson, L. S., *Profitable Farm Management and Marketing*, Lippincott, Philadelphia, 1929, Chapter XI.

Taylor, H. C., Tolley, H. M., and Tapp, J. W., *Practical Farm Economics*, Government Printing Office, Washington, 1924, Chapter VII.

Warren, G. F., *Farm Management*, Macmillan, New York, 1916, Chapter XI.

Michigan Special Bulletin 241: "A Farm Management Study of Crop Production Practices," by P. G. Minneman and E. B. Hill, 1933.

Minnesota Bulletin 205: "A Study of Farm Organization in Southwestern Minnesota," by George A. Pond and Jesse W. Tapp, 1923.

Pennsylvania Bulletin 292: "Labor Requirements for Pennsylvania Farms," by J. E. McCord and C. E. Cronemeyer, 1933.

U. S. Department of Agriculture, Department Bulletin 1285: "Truck Farm Labor in New Jersey, 1922," by Josiah C. Folsom, 1925.

CHAPTER XXI

Checking up on Performance—Use of Records

The Problem: How can a farmer find out if his budgetary plans are being carried out? Can he use his accounts and records as guide from month to month, or must he wait until the end of the year to get any useful information from them?

Current Use of the Financial Records

The farmer starts out at the beginning of the year with a fairly definite plan or budget. As the year goes on he should check up to see if he is following these plans. At the end of the year he will compare the plans with the final results, so that he may have a better basis for planning the following year. To do this he must have definite records of farm performance. A third, but related, need for records may occur during the year if changed prices or weather conditions make it necessary to revise plans. It is much easier to plan changes if one already knows what he is doing.

The accounts and budgets should be organized so they conform to each other. In this chapter we will consider how we can use the various records to help reach the goal set up by the plan or budget.

From month to month the farmer should watch the figures in the financial records. The monthly or quarterly income and expense figures will show if the farm is performing as it was expected to in the budgetary plans. These figures will also forewarn him of any shortage of funds. Comparisons should be made with the corresponding month of the preceding year. This monthly comparison will show if the receipts from such items as cream or milk sales are as large as expected and are keeping up with those of the same season the year before. Some farm sales, such as those of hogs or cattle, may occur in one month one year and a different one the next. In comparisons of monthly receipts allowance should of course be made for such variation. Comparison of quarterly totals is apt to be more satisfactory, because they differ less from year to year and because they cover a longer period of time.

Operating expenses are the most helpful to compare on the expense side of the accounts. These expenses, including hired labor, equipment upkeep and repairs, feeds bought, and so on can, to some extent, be controlled. Consequently they are the ones to watch most closely from month to month. The fixed expenses, such as taxes or interest on mortgages, are beyond the farmer's immediate control.

There is usually seasonal variation in both income and expenses. Comparisons should, therefore, be made with the corresponding period of the preceding year rather than with other periods of the same year. At certain times of the year considerable labor is hired, at others little or none. During the pasture season income from dairy products is usually greater than during the winter. There is a similar seasonal cycle in the sale of poultry products. One reason for watching the records from month to month is to find out if it would not be possible to change this cycle somewhat by producing for the market at a different season.

Current Use of Physical Production Records

Even before crops or livestock are sold, it is helpful to check up on the progress of the enterprise.   If the farmer waits until the product is sold, the best he can do is to try to avoid making the same mistakes again.

Fig. 58.—Weighing milk to check up on the performance of the dairy herd.

The physical production records should be planned to suit the peculiar problems of each enterprise.   Most of them, however, are already available either from the financial records or from other sources.   The records of cream and milk sales which are kept with the financial accounts give the needed information on the dairy enterprise.   As the receipts from dairy products are entered each month, it is a good habit to look back at the amount of butterfat sold the corresponding month of the previous year. In this way it is easy to see if the cows are producing as well this year as last. If not, an effort should be made to improve the rations or otherwise stimulate production.

The record of egg sales will do for comparison on the poultry enterprise. With both dairy stock and poultry the seasonal cycle of production should be kept in mind and comparisons should be made with the corresponding month of the preceding year as well as the past month.

With the fattening of cattle or hogs, a slightly different method should be used. If there is a set of scales on the farm, the best method is to weigh the stock, perhaps once a month, while they are in the feed lot. These weights should be recorded for comparison with weights the preceding and following months. The daily rate of gain should be noted and compared with what is considered a satisfactory standard for that type of stock. The amount of gain should also be compared with the amount of feed consumed. The rate of gain per day will decrease as the stock fattens. The value of the gain and of the feed should be compared to see if a satisfactory margin over feed cost is being made.

Analyzing Records at the End of the Year

If the proper records have been kept, it is possible at the end of the year to check over the operation of the entire farm. Just what did each enterprise add to the net income? Which enterprises were efficiently handled and which did badly because of unsatisfactory methods? What can be done to increase returns next year? Such questions can be answered when the records are completed and summarized.

Joining a coöperative farm record group or studying comparable figures from the agricultural experiment station will help the farmer greatly with the problems of his own particular farm. While no two farms are identical, the principal enterprises will be very similar to those on neighboring farms.

Net income measures the success of the whole farm. The analysis of farm record data generally starts out with the figures for the net return of the whole farm as a measure of the success of the combined enterprises. This should be compared with the net income of the preceding year and also with net income on similar farms in the neighborhood if possible. Next a similar comparison is made of the various financial ratios and of other indices which bring out relationships between investment, amount of business done, and income.

After this the enterprises or groups of enterprises are studied one by one to check up on performance in each branch of the business. The cropping system comes first with records of acreages and yields of each crop. Next comes the livestock system, which may be used to dispose of feed crops raised. Third, we consider the efficiency with which labor and power is used. Table XLVII gives an example of such data.

Two methods of comparison. There are two possible lines of analysis or comparison that might be followed by the farmer who is studying over his records at the end of the year. He may confine his attention to his own farm, as he will have to do if he can get no data from comparable farm records for his neighborhood, or he may compare the figures from his farm with similar figures or averages from other farms. This is often possible where averages or standards are being prepared by coöperative farm rec-

TABLE XLVII

ANALYTICAL DATA FROM FARM RECORDS[a]

	This Farm		Group Average		
	Last Year	This Year	This Year	Last Year	Source[b]
Financial Factors:					
Management return, dollars ..	1,127	−1,406	−1,634	865	F
Net farm income, dollars.....	3,200	787	561	3,132	F
Gross income per $100 investment, dollars..............	15.73	12.16	9.28	15.86	F & I
Operating Expense per $100 gross income, dollars.......	10.61	12.11	16.57		F & I
Fixed Expense per $100 gross income, dollars...........	11.51	18.14	17.36	41.00	F & I
Size of Farm:					
Total capital managed, dollars.	41,238	39,048	36,278	37,600	I
Gross farm income, dollars....	5,505	5,044	5,873	7,433	F
Total acres.................	152	152	181	189	C
Crop acres.................	114	115	150	161	C
Months man labor...........	14	16	17½	17	S
Cropping System:					
Crop value per acre rotation, dollars...................	30	18	17	26	C
Acres corn..................	58	53	76	75	C
Yield corn per acre, bushels...	53	41	38	48	C
Acres oats	44	46	47	52	C
Yield oats per acre, bushels...	52	50	50	52	C
Acres in hay................	8	10	8	13	C
Yield hay per acre, tons......	3.3	2.1	2.0	2.1	C
Livestock:					
Average livestock income per $100 feed, dollars..........	124	118	110	136	F & Fe
Hogs:					
Returns per $100 feed, dollars	114	122	121	122	F & Fe
No. litters.................	16	14	12	13	L
Pounds pork per litter.....	1,851	1,862	1,435	1,517	L
Gain per day, spring pigs...	1.1	1.0	.9	.95	L
Pounds feed per 100 pounds gain...................	526	393	467	484	L & Fe
Cattle:					
Returns per $100 feed, dollars	125	102	98	...	F & Fe
No. milk cows............	7	8	4.5	6.6	L
No. beef cows.............	4	2	4	2.3	L
Pounds B. F. per milk cow..	280	243	193	186	L
Pounds beef per beef cow...	877	736	591	659	L
Poultry:					
No. hens.................	161	173	163	125	L
Eggs per hen..............	104	113	102	92	L
Total income per hen, dollars	5.06	4.14	2.78	3.59	F & L
Use of Labor and Power:					
Crop acres per man.........	98	88	101	102	C & S
Crop acres per horse........	28	26	29	30	C & S
Machine cost per crop acres, dollars...................	1.34	1.20	1.26	1.61	F, C, & S
Power cost per crop acres, dollars...................	5.73	6.04	5.39	7.40	F, C, & S
Livestock income per man, dollars...................	4,212	2,568	1,982	2,549	F & S
Gross income per man, dollars.	4,718	3,784	2,482	4,248	F & S

[a] Methods of computing these efficiency factors are described in the summary pages of the Iowa Columnar Farm Records.

[b] Abbreviations for records used in analysis: F—financial record; I—Inventories; C—crop production records; L—livestock production record; Fe—feed record; S—supplementary information.

ord associations, agricultural experiment stations or agricultural teachers. The farmer who has just finished his first year of record keeping will have to depend on this sort of comparison.

Both methods are very useful, although they do not show quite the same things. A comparison with other farms is needed to show the farmer where he stands in general efficiency. He cannot form any definite idea of this without comparing his results with those of other farmers. Comparison with other records of the same year gives a clear picture of performance under the same weather and price conditions. Comparison with crop yields or income on the same farm the year before always leaves some doubt as to how much of the difference should be attributed to different weather or price conditions and how much to difference in efficiency.

A comparison only with other farms cannot, however, be entirely satisfactory, because no two farms are identical. The farmer is most interested in the progress he is making on his own particular farm. A sort of three-way comparison is the most complete analysis of the records. The farmer should first compare his results with those of last year. Then he should compare his results with those of other neighboring farms for this year. Finally he should compare his improvements in efficiency with the changes that these neighboring farmers have made.

Example of Analysis of Farm Records—Financial Factors

Table XLVII gives some of the more important figures from the records of a farm in the Iowa cash grain area. For comparison, averages are given for a group of 49 farms as well as the figures from the same farm for the preceding year. During the year for which figures are given there was a sharp decline in prices of crops and livestock. Because of this the net income for nearly all farms was reduced.

The net income for this farm was $787 and the average for the group was $561. During the preceding year the net income for the farm had been $3,200, and $3,132 the average for all the farms. The decline of $2,250 on this farm was chiefly due to the fall in price of crops and livestock. The gross income per $100 invested in the business was $12.16 and had been $15.73 the year before. The average for the whole group was $9.28. Since expenses have not fallen as rapidly as gross income, the fixed and operating expenses are higher in proportion. Operating expenses were $12.11 per $100 of income and in the past year $10.61, both of which are satisfactory figures. Fixed expenses have increased from $11.51 to $18.14, because more money had been spent on improvements.

This farm consists of 152 acres, of which 115 were in crops. The average size of the group was 181 acres, with 150 acres in crops. The total capital managed by this farmer amounted to $39,048, about $1,200 less than the year before. Since the capital valuation of this farm is higher than the average of the group, it is evidently of a better grade of land or is better equipped.

In spite of its higher capital valuation, the gross income is only $5,044 compared to $5,873 for the group of farms. Evidently the investment on this farm is not yielding as high a rate of return as the neighboring farms. What are the reasons for this? For one thing this farm was operated with a total of 16 months' labor compared to $17\frac{1}{2}$ months for the group average. Remember that neither

the amount of land nor the amount of capital alone measures the size of the farm.   Labor, too, is an element of
size, and if wisely used it helps to enlarge the income.
In making such an analysis it is necessary to draw on
all the farm records available.   In Table XLVII sources
of the various figures are noted at the right hand side of
the table.   Notice that financial accounts and inventories
provide only the first seven items, which deal with the net
returns and investment in the business.   Crop-produc-
tion records and livestock-production records give us the
information necessary to size up crop- and livestock-
production enterprises.

Data from feed records must be added to give us a definite idea of the success of the livestock enterprises.
Financial information and the farmers' general knowledge
were used in measuring the efficiency with which labor
and power were used.   Many of the most valuable indices
are obtained by combining figures from two or even three
different records.   It is both interesting and instructive
to check over this list of efficiency factors and see just
how many could be got from a financial record alone.

The cropping system.   The cropping system is the
logical place to start in studying individual enterprises,
since it provides the feed on which the livestock system is
based.   The rotation should be reconsidered to see if any
change might lead to a greater total production of feeds
or cash crops, or if some new crop might be substituted to
reduce the labor demand in the peak seasons.   The chief
question is the total amount and value of crops produced.

The value of crops on the farm we have been discussing
amounted to $18 per acre in rotation, and $30 the preceding year.   This is better than for the entire group, which
averaged $17, and $26 last year.   Most of the difference

between years is due to lower crop prices, but also the summer had been dry and yields were low. Nevertheless, the farmer should question whether or not he might, by increasing his efficiency, get higher yields next year.

How do the acres in crops compare with the average of farms in the neighborhood? On this farm there were 53 acres of corn and 46 acres of oats compared to 76 acres of corn and 47 acres of oats on the average farm of the group. The higher proportion of oats is fairly sure to lower the total amount of feed raised and the average value per acre. Would it be possible to substitute a higher yielding crop for some of the oats? Some farmers have been planting a mixture of oats, barley, and wheat and getting a larger yield of feed per acre. Could this be tried on this particular farm?

Livestock enterprises. Livestock enterprises should be analyzed next. Note first the general results of the entire livestock system. What return was obtained per $100 of feed for hogs, cattle, or other producing animals? Since feed makes up about 75 per cent of the total cost of livestock production, the return per $100 of feed should be about $133 if the farmer is to break even on the combined livestock enterprises over a long period of time. On this farm it amounted to $118, which means that only small returns were received from labor and the use of the buildings and equipment. The average for the group of farms was $110 and the returns on the same farm $124 the preceding year. Under unfavorable price conditions, however, it is better to make small returns from labor and buildings than none at all.

The hog enterprise. Hogs are the most important livestock on this farm. Fourteen litters of pigs were raised, as compared to sixteen the year before and an average of twelve for the group. Returns per $100 of feed were $122, as compared to $114 the year before and $121 for the 49 farms. Evidently there has been an improvement in returns even though prices declined. How did the farmer accomplish this?

Let us check up first on the physical performance of the enterprise. Rates of gain and of feed consumption give a direct indication of the farmer's efficiency, since they are not affected by price changes. First the live pork produced per sow bred was 1,862 pounds compared to 1,435 pounds average for the group of farms. This was done partly by raising more pigs per litter and partly by raising more fall litters than were raised on the average farm. This means a worthwhile saving on the keep of the breeding herd and consequently lower cost per pig. The production per sow was almost as large the year before, however, so this is not the cause for improvement.

Now let us note the rate of gain per pig per day. This was also satisfactory, amounting to one pound per day, compared to 1.1 the year before and .9 pound on the average farm. How about the amount of concentrates fed per 100 pounds of gain? Here we find where the improvement in returns came from. On this farm 100 pounds of gain were obtained from only 393 pounds of grain, as compared to 526 pounds on this farm the year before. The average amount used on the group of farms was 467 pounds How was this saving of feed accomplished? In both years scrupulous attention was given to disease prevention. This year, however, more thought was given to balancing the hogs' rations, and they were fed more protein supplements. Also they had a good alfalfa pasture instead of the rather poor pasture of the year before. The saving in total feed consumption is therefore not as large as it appears, but alfalfa pasture is cheaper than corn and the hogs made good gains on it. These figures show the farmer in an impressive way the results he got from his change of methods and indicate satisfactory results from the hogs. In making these comparisons, the average of the neighbors is not necessarily a satisfactory standard of accomplishment. Such figures are used because they do provide a fairly definite means of comparison under similar price and weather conditions.

The cattle enterprise. The dual-purpose cattle enterprise found on this farm is somewhat more difficult to analyze than the hog enterprise or a straight beef or dairy enterprise. With dual-purpose cattle there are two products instead of one to consider.

On this farm eight cows were milked and two kept for stock instead of the seven milk and four stock cows the year before. This indicates more attention to dairy production, but the amount of butterfat per cow was only 243 pounds instead of the 280 of the year before. Both these figures are higher than the average of 193 pounds for the group. This lower figure may indicate that some of the poorer cows had been milked this year but not the year before. Beef production per cow has declined, however, perhaps as a result of less attention to that side of the enterprise. Has this change in emphasis been profitable?

The returns per $100 of feed have declined from $125 to $102, partly as a result of lower prices in the more recent year. This is a slightly higher average return per $100 of feed than for the group of farms, but in neither year has it been high enough to afford the usual margin over feed costs.

Poultry. This farm has been keeping about the average number of hens, but the number of eggs per hen has been slightly higher than for the group of farms. The returns per hen from both eggs and poultry sales have been about 50 per cent higher than the average, showing very satisfactory results from this enterprise.   Should it be enlarged to take advantage of this opportunity for profit?

Use of Labor and Power

Economy and efficiency in the use of cost factors is just as necessary to maximum profit as efficiency in the income-yielding enterprises.   The use of labor and power are two of the most important expense elements.   This farm was operated by the owner plus the equivalent of about two months' help from members of the family and two months' hired labor.   An average of 88 acres of crops were handled per 12 months of labor compared to 98 acres the year before and 101 average for the group.   Did the increased yields and value of crops justify this greater amount of labor per acre?

The power has been provided by a tractor and four horses, with a fifth horse part of the year.   The number of acres of crops handled per horse was slightly lower than the average of the group of farms, which of course increases a little the cost of producing the crops.   How could the power cost have been reduced on a farm of this size?

The acres of crops per man is not a complete measure of the efficiency of the labor, because livestock also needs attention.   The livestock income per man (that is per 12 months of labor) is used to indicate the amount of livestock production per man.   This amounted to $2,568, compared to $1,982 for the group.   The total income per man was $3,784, compared to $2,482 for the group.   Considering both crop and livestock income, we find that this farmer has obtained a greater income than the average for the use of his labor. Remember, though, that income is produced by all the factors of production and not merely by labor.

Diminishing Returns as Shown by the Records

Obtaining the highest possible value from any *one* efficiency factor is not always desirable. Nearly any one of the factors of production may be forced up to, or past, the point of marginal returns. For example, where the percentage of investment in current and working assets is somewhat greater than average, there is generally a larger net income. But if too large a percentage is invested in machinery or livestock, the most advantageous balance between current and fixed investment is lost and the farm is said to be over-stocked or over-equipped. Handling a large acreage of crops per man is desirable, but if the labor is spread too thinly over a very large acreage, the income is likely to be decreased instead of increased.

If livestock production per cow or per sow is forced to extremely high figures, this may become an unfavorable instead of a favorable indication. A very high rate of return per $100 of feed (for example, $200 or more) generally means that the farmer is concentrating too much of his time on small livestock enterprises or else is neglecting other phases of the business in order to make the best possible showing on livestock. He should first check over the figures from his records to see if he is keeping up to a satisfactory standard. He should also consider whether or not he has pushed efficiency so far in one direction that he has incurred a loss in another.

Reference

Hopkins, John A., *Farm Records*, Collegiate Press, Ames, Iowa, 1936, Chapters 10-14.

CHAPTER XXII

Modifying the Budget and Allowing for Price Changes

The Problem: How can a farmer modify his budget in order to take advantage of the information he has gained from his year's records? How shall he take price changes into account in planning for the following year?

Using the Records to Improve the Budget

A farmer usually has to base his first year's plans on his general knowledge, because he has no records of his own managerial ability and probably none for the farm on which he is beginning operations. After farming for a year, he is much better able to judge what his farm and he himself can do. If he has kept records this information will be more adequate and precise. The farmer will nearly always want to make some changes after a year or two of experience, or after the summary of his farm records becomes available.

He may make some changes because of new information about the productivity of his land or his ability in getting milk production or gains on his livestock. In the preceding chapter we discussed the process of examining the various phases of the business.

After this analysis, the farmer should see if other crops could be substituted for those which did not yield well or could not be disposed of at a profit. If the oat crop was unprofitable, could it be replaced by barley as a feed crop or perhaps by wheat as a cash crop? What problems would have to be considered in replacing oats with barley? With winter wheat?

If one of the livestock projects is not bringing in a satisfactory return, could the methods of handling it be improved? Would it be better to replace it with some other project? Is the kind of power, horses or tractor, now in use the most economical for that particular farm?

Changing Prices and Budgetary Modification

Price changes are a most important reason for making changes in the farm plans. When the plans were first made, they were based on a certain set of prices for farm products and also of prices for feeds, fertilizers, and labor. But these prices are constantly changing, so it is necessary to change plans, also, in order to get the maximum return from the farm. This seldom means dropping one enterprise entirely and taking on another in its place. More often it means that the enterprise whose price has fallen should be reduced while another with more favorable prices should be enlarged a bit. Many enterprises are more or less dependent on others for raw materials. Some are adopted to round out the labor schedule. A small change in the size of an enterprise may be enough to reduce direct outlays to a minimum and use resources most profitably.

The accounts of the year just closed show what earnings were under the prices of that year. Next year's prices will be different. The farmer who plans his operations to fit last year's prices will always be just a year behind time. *He should try to anticipate prices as far as he can.* No one can do this exactly, but by studying price trends and the production forecasts of the U. S. Department of Agriculture, he can usually anticipate the general direction of change.

Types of Price Changes

Seasonal movements. In order to interpret the price outlook, the farmer should know the principal types of price movement. The seasonal movement is probably the most familiar. This more or less regular variation recurs each year with the cycle of the seasons. Thus, grain prices usually decline each year just before harvest time and then, after the bulk of the crop has moved to market, gradually work upwards until the next harvest. Livestock prices follow similar fluctuations. During the months when movements to market are heaviest, the supplies of meat may be more than consumers will buy at prevailing prices. Prices must, therefore, decline until it is profitable to put the surplus into storage.

Seasonal movements are not always uniform. A crop may be harvested a week or so earlier or later than usual because of weather conditions. For one reason or another, livestock may move to market earlier one year than the next. The yield of a fresh vegetable may be large in the early producing area and small in the late crop area. Other influences may also cause fluctuations strong enough to hide the seasonal movement.

Long-time trends. The long-time (or secular) movement of prices is one the ordinary farmer may not be aware of. The price of a commodity or group of commodities may work slowly upward or downward for a period of ten or twenty years. Since the yearly change is small, most people are likely not to notice this movement unless it is brought to their attention.

Long-time movements in prices may come from various sources. Increases in the gold supply, or its failure to keep up with the growth of business, have caused prices to drift upward or downward for long periods of years in the past. At the same time gradual improvement in methods of production have caused larger outputs and accordingly lower prices of some products. In the early part of the twentieth century the more rapid growth of population in

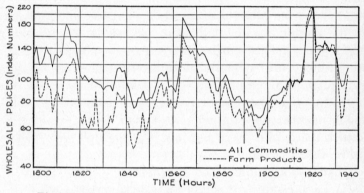

Fig. 59.—Long-time trend in farm prices—1800 to 1935.

the cities than in the agricultural area caused agricultural prices to rise faster than those of most industrial products.

Cyclical fluctuations. A third type of movement is found in price cycles. These are wavelike variations in prices or other data which rise to a peak and then decline to a low point at more or less regular intervals. The cyclical fluctuations, however, are not represented by a smooth curve with equal distances between peaks or troughs, as the beginner may imagine. The "hog price cycle" is probably the one most familiar to the well-read farmer. If monthly or yearly prices of hogs are plotted on graph paper they will be found to rise and fall usually at intervals of four to six years.   But neither the length of time nor the amount of fluctuation in the cycles is at all uniform.   In fact, some who have studied hog prices most carefully doubt that anything like a regular cycle exists. When many so-called "cyclical" movements are studied closely they are found to be really of the "episodic" type.

Movements caused by specific episodes or events. Powerful natural or social happenings, such as wars, floods, strikes, droughts, and so on, disturb economic relationships and cause what are known as "episodic" movements of prices and production figures.   A war of any size causes shortages of materials used in manufacturing munitions or in feeding or clothing the armies.   The results do not end with the war itself, but are likely to last in one form or another for several years afterwards while the industries that were thrown out of their usual courses are getting back into their normal relationships with each other.

Chance variation.   The accidental or unexplained variation is the fifth type.   From day to day and week to week there are continual small fluctuations in prices or in amounts of produce received at markets.   Some of these can be explained if a study is made.   Others seem to occur without any apparent reason.

Relative Rather than Absolute Prices Serve as a Guide

Even with these various types of price movements in mind, and with fairly definite ideas about probable trends, the farmer will not plan his farm operations on the basis of absolute prices.   He will rather base his plans on the *relative* price of each product as compared to other products he might raise.   Considering the hog enterprise by itself, we find that it would probably be more profitable to raise hogs when corn is 30 cents per bushel and hogs $4 than when hogs are $8 and corn $1 per bushel. The possible returns from feeding other livestock should be considered, as well as the prices of the corn and hogs. Steer feeding may be more profitable than hog raising when the steers are selling at $10 with a $2 margin over feeders, and hogs are $6. But if the feeder margin falls to $1.50 and the price of fat steers to $7.50, while hogs rise to $7, it may be more profitable to increase the number of hogs and not feed steers.

It is not necessarily more profitable to raise wheat at $1.00 than when it is 80 cents. If labor, fertilizer, and farm machinery prices are still lower in proportion, the wheat may yield a greater return during the period of lower prices.

Remember that the farmer cannot plan his program one crop at a time. The entire farm must be planned as a whole in order to get the greatest net return for the use of his combined resources. The question is not so much whether it will be profitable to grow a certain crop as whether one crop will bring a larger return than some other which could be raised instead. With livestock, the problem is to decide which type of livestock will be the most profitable means of disposing of the available feed and labor.

Modifying the Crop Program

Price changes sometimes call for a revision of plans after the year's operations are already started. For example, a farmer who has been selling part of his small grain notes that the price of oats has fallen to 30 cents. The outlook is for 44 bushels per acre. The price of barley is 50 cents and seems likely to remain at about that figure.   His neighbor has been raising 30 bushels of barley per acre.   The oat crop thus promises to be worth about $12 per acre and the barley $15.   In this case it is easy to change the plan.   Both oats and barley are spring crops and require about the same amount of labor at the same seasons, so barley can be substituted for at least part of the oats.

Suppose that the alternative crop were winter wheat. Several new considerations now come into the problem. Can the land be cleared of corn in the fall in time to plant the wheat?   Will this work interfere with the other labor plans?   In making this choice, too, the decision would have to be made in early fall, while the decision to plant barley could be made in late winter or early spring.

Other decisions calling for prompt action must be made when a crop is not doing well during the growing season. Suppose an insect pest attacks the crop.   Should the farmer continue to raise the half crop that remains or should he plow it up and put in an emergency crop? The probable value of the remaining damaged crop must be compared with the value of the emergency crop minus the additional costs.   Most farmers have had experience with winter killing of a seeding of clover or alfalfa.   In such a case other plans must be made in order to have hay for cattle and horses.   Will an emergency crop such as soy beans or sudan grass yield a satisfactory hay crop?   Here the deciding factor will probably be the amount of hay that can be raised rather than the market prices of the two crops.

Influence of Price Changes on Livestock Plans

Whenever relative prices of livestock change, the advantage in producing a certain kind of livestock or live-

stock product changes also. Changes in prices alter the
advantage in livestock production over the direct sale of
crops.

Let us suppose a farmer is making his feeding plans for
next year in the fall, when he knows how much corn he
has. He can summarize his feed record on a carload of
steers fed last year. From his record he can also tell
about what the total feed requirements will be for the
spring pigs he will market in a few weeks. How shall he
decide whether to feed steers again next year or to breed
more sows?

First he will need to estimate the probable prices of
hogs and steers during the coming year. From reports of
the number of cattle shipped into feeding areas and the
outlook report he believes that cattle prices will be definitely lower next year. Feeder cattle are selling for $6
per 100 pounds instead of the $7 of a year ago. Lower
prices seem probable for finished steers, perhaps $7.50 in-
stead of the $9 at which his last load was sold. He ex-
pects feed to be about the same price as last year.

Another carload of steers would probably make about
the same rates of gain on the same amount of feed as last
year. These figures are shown in Table XLVIII. The
cattle had used about 675 bushels of corn and 15 tons of
ensilage, containing about 75 more bushels of corn. They
also consumed six tons of alfalfa and two tons of linseed
oil meal. The total gain was 300 pounds per head, 6,000
pounds in all. The increase in price over their purchase
price was $820. The total value of feed was $562, which
left $258 to pay for labor and use of equipment.

The same amount of corn plus the use of the alfalfa for
pasture for hogs and 1½ tons of tankage would feed about
eight litters of six pigs each. At 220 pounds these would

Table XLVIII

EXAMPLE OF COMPARISON OF STEER VS. HOG FEEDING OPERATION

Steer Feeding Enterprise

	Last Year	Current Year (estimates)
Stock:		
Number of steers..............	20	20
Weight when bought, pounds per head........................	700	700
Weight when sold, pounds per head........................	1,000	1,000
Gain per head, pounds........	300	300
Total gain, pounds............	6,000	6,000
Price when bought, per 100 pounds, dollars.............	7.00	6.00
Price when sold, per 100 pounds, dollars.....................	9.00	7.50
Total purchase price, dollars....	980.00	840.00
Total sale price, dollars........	1,800.00	1,500.00
Net increase in value, dollars...	820.00	660.00
Feed:		
Bushels of Corn, @ .50........	675	675
Tons silage, @ $4.00..........	15	15
Tons alfalfa hay, @ $14.00.....	6	6
Tons linseed oil meal, @ $40.00.	2	2
Total value feed, dollars.......	562.00	562.00
Value of production above feed, dollars.....................	258.00	98.00

Estimates on Hog Enterprise

		Current Year
Stock:		
Number litters to replace 20 steers........		8
Number pigs...........................		48
Total pounds gain, @ 220 lbs. per pig.....		10,500
Value hogs, @ $6.50 per 100 pounds.......	$686.00	
Feed:		
Corn, @ $.50 per bushel, number of bushels		750
Tankage, @ $45 per ton, number of pounds		3,000
Acres alfalfa pasture.....................		3
Total value of feed, dollars..............	527.00	
Value of production above feed, dollars....	159.00	

total 10,560, and would bring in $686 at present prices. Their feed would be worth $527, and would leave $159 to pay for the labor and use of equipment.

If steers are fed next year, bought at $6 and sold at $7.50, according to the farmer's expectations, they would return only $98 above the price of the feed. At these prices hogs would bring in $61 more than the steers.

The decision to feed hogs instead of steers could not, of course, be made on a basis of price alone. Perhaps the hog equipment is not adequate to take care of so many additional hogs. The farmer may even decide that $159 is not enough return for his labor and may sell the crop directly. This last is not very likely, however. A stronger reason for feeding steers where there is clover or mixed hay is to utilize the roughage that cannot be fed to hogs or sold directly. Some hogs will probably be kept, anyway, to follow the steers. Even if the $159 does not equal the going rates for wages and interest on investment in equipment, it is still better to take that amount of return for labor and interest than to get nothing at all.

Modifying livestock plans during the year. Let us suppose that the farmer is feeding a carload of steers that have been in his feed lot three or four months. He has also ten litters of pigs from six weeks to two months old. Now the price of fat cattle goes down one dollar per hundred pounds, with prospects for further decline. The price of hogs and the report on size of hog crop promises a strong hog market for the coming months. How much can the farmer alter his plans at this late date?

The steers can be sold at a lighter weight than he had intended. This will of course mean a lower price than they would bring in prime condition, but each additional hundred pounds of gain takes more feed than the preceding one. If a gain of only 250 instead of 300 pounds were put on each steer, the farmer would save more than one-sixth of his feed.

Hogs had been fed to about 220 pounds. The last few pounds of gain on them also costs more than the earlier gains. If they are fed on the grain saved by selling the steers at lighter weight they might be sold at 250 instead of 220 pounds. If corn prices are relatively high, it might be more profitable to sell the corn as grain. In deciding such a problem as this, the prices of each kind of stock, the price of the corn, and also the amount of gain on the livestock must all be considered.

References

Hopkins, John A., *Farm Records,* Collegiate Press, Ames, Iowa, 1936, Chapter XXI.

U. S. Department of Agriculture, Farmers' Bulletin 1564: "Farm Budgeting," by J. B. Hutson, 1928.

Part VIII

EXTERNAL RELATIONSHIPS OF THE FARM BUSINESS

CHAPTER XXIII

Coöperation in Current Farm Management

The Problem: Are there any farm jobs that can best be done in coöperation with some of the neighbors? Is coöperation more satisfactory than hiring extra labor or special outfits for threshing or silo filling? How far should coöperation with other farmers be carried in actual farm operation?

The Farmer's Relation with Others

So far we have been concerned almost entirely with relationships within the farm business itself. But the farmer's success also depends on how well he adjusts his business to his neighbors and to the other businesses with which he deals. In the first place, he may find it advantageous to do certain farm work in coöperation with his neighbors. Second, he must be able to buy and sell to the best advantage and to make satisfactory arrangements with bankers and various professional men whose services he needs.

There are really a surprising number of things that the farmer can accomplish by working with his neighbors that either he could not do at all by himself, or at least could not do so economically or so well.

The first kind of coöperation we are apt to think of in farm management is the exchange of labor for jobs which require large crews of men. A second type is the cooperative ownership of pieces of machinery too large for the individual farm. A third is the coöperative ownership of breeding animals. There are, in addition, coöperative marketing organizations, where the marketing arrangements are delegated to someone specially trained for that particular job. One person spending all his time at the work can usually perform the service better and more cheaply than can several men who spend only a little time and at widely separated intervals during the year. This is also true of cow-testing associations, farm-accounting associations, and similar groups.

Coöperation by Exchange of Labor

Many farmers coöperate by exchanging labor, generally on jobs which cannot be done effectively by working alone. Threshing and silo filling are two common examples. From three to a dozen farmers, the number depending on the size of the grain separator, work together on the threshing. This means that each man spends one or two weeks, with one or more teams, working with the threshing outfit, or else hires a man to send in his place. In many sections of the country there is a slack season around threshing time and the farmer can spend his own time with the threshing outfit and save a cash outlay.

Silo filling also takes extra labor and teams, and is usually managed in about the same way as threshing, but by a smaller group of men. Farmers also exchange labor for haying and various other jobs. The saving in labor bills and the advantage of more efficient help is generally very worth while.

Hauling milk is another way of coöperating to save labor. Two or three neighbors who sell their milk to the same creamery or ship from the same station often find it advantageous to take turns in hauling, usually for a week at a time. A coöperative creamery is a further form of coöperation, but one that is ordinarily associated with marketing rather than farm operation.

Courtesy Minneapolis-Moline Power Implement Co.

Fig. 60.—Farmers often coöperate in silo filling.

When labor is traded there should be a clear understanding about how it is to be returned. Usually it is simply understood that an equal number of day's work is to be returned, but sometimes the particular time and job is definitely agreed upon. This is important when the work is going to be critically needed at a certain time. Thus, a farmer may agree to help a neighbor get in a cutting of alfalfa if he can have help in return in filling his silo.

Often the labor exchanged is not equal in amount. Sometimes the man giving the least help agrees to furnish the rest of the labor when needed, and sometimes a cash settlement is made. If this is to be done, the method and rate of settlement should be agreed upon before any great difference in the amount of work has developed.

Coöperation in Ownership of Equipment

Joint ownership of pieces of equipment is another common way of coöperating in farm operation. Such large and expensive pieces as grain separators, combines, corn pickers, and silage cutters which cannot usually be used economically on a single farm are often owned in this way. The terms of such ownership vary considerably. Sometimes each man puts an equal amount into the purchase price, sometimes the investment is in proportion to the number of acres of that particular crop each grows. Or one man may purchase the machine and his neighbor provide the tractor to pull it.

An expensive piece of machinery, such as a combine or corn picker, should be kept in repair by a competent mechanic. Agreement should be made beforehand as to how and when needed repairs are to be paid for. Repairs are sometime charged to the man on whose farm the breakdown occurred, but a better method is to pool all the year's repair expenses and pay for them in proportion to the number of acres the machine covered on each man's farm. In this way there is not the tendency to neglect a replacement until the machine actually breaks down. Also, the farmer on whose place the machine happened to break will not feel that he has been imposed on by the preceding men who neglected to provide needed repairs. Fuel, oil, grease, and twine, however, should be paid for separately by each individual.

If possible, the same man should continue to operate the machine throughout the season on all the farms. It usually takes some time to develop the knack of handling such a machine as a combine. The man who seems to do it best should be given the job of operating and caring for it the entire season, in order to get the best work done and to take the best care of the machine.

Coöperative ownership is not confined to expensive equipment. Farmers often coöperate in buying smaller machines that are used for only a few days during the year. Such machines as grain drills, silage cutters, potato planters or diggers, spray outfits and so on are commonly owned by two or more farmers.

Borrowing such pieces of equipment from neighbors may or may not be satisfactory. The neighbor who has a grain drill may be using it himself, and the farmer who depends on borrowing may be late in getting his crop in and thus lose more than he saves in interest and depreciation. Coöperation ownership or a definite agreement to hire the equipment is usually more satisfactory to everyone concerned.

Coöperative Ownership of Breeding Sires

Improvement of livestock requires both time and expense. The farmer who depends on his own resources alone may have to make shift with an inferior quality of breeding stock. This means that future production will also be inferior.

It is possible, on the other hand, to buy a well-bred bull, boar, or ram in coöperation with a neighbor at little more investment for each than the cost of a scrub sire. The expense may be even less, and the returns will certainly be more satisfactory.

Before purchasing a sire coöperatively, the farmers should come to a definite understanding about how expenses are to be shared. If the animal is to be kept at one farm all the time, there should be an agreement about providing feed and care. If, as is often done, the sire is to be kept part of the time on one farm and an equal length of time on another, this should also be agreed definitely. A duplicate written agreement stating the duty of each party will usually prevent misunderstandings.

Another means of coöperation is for each farmer to buy a high-grade sire and, after using it as long as seems desirable, trade with the neighbor. In this way each will have the use of a proven sire and the outlay for purchase of new ones will be greatly reduced. For smaller herds, coöperative ownership is likely to prove most satisfactory, since it divides the current expense of keeping the sire. For larger herds, each of which needs a sire, trading provides the same advantage as coöperative ownership in reducing original investment and obtaining the use of a proven sire.

The Cow-Testing Association

The purpose of the cow-testing association is to obtain a record of the performance of each individual cow in the herd.   In this way the less productive cows are culled out and the herd improved.   The testing is done by a man

Fig. 61.—The cow-testing association provides a valuable coöperative service.

who has been trained under the supervision of the state agricultural extension service.   The project is supervised by the extension service in coöperation with the U. S. Department of Agriculture.   The associations are composed of 24 to 26 farms, so the tester can spend one day per month on each one.   Here he weighs the milk of each cow and also makes a butterfat test of a composite sample of each cow's night and morning milk.   This is considered an average of the month and is used to compute the total production.

A feed record is combined with the milk record, and on each visit the tester weighs the grain and roughage fed each cow. Local feed prices are applied to the recorded feed consumption in order to get an idea of the return each cow is making above her feed cost. The number of pounds of feed consumed per pound of butterfat or per hundred pounds of milk is also computed. These figures are made available by the extension service or by the Bureau of Animal Industry.

Coöperative Farm Management Association

The individual farmer finds it difficult to evaluate the performance of his business. While he is thoroughly familiar with the details of his own farm, he has no means of comparing his results with those of other farmers. Nor is he likely to be acquainted with the most complete and up-to-date methods of keeping and analyzing accounts and records.

The coöperative farm accounting or farm management association is very valuable in overcoming this lack of information. These associations consist of a minimum of 100 to a maximum of 200 farmers who employ a trained farm management specialist to supervise and analyze their records, to check over the practices they are using, and to talk over their managerial problems. The actual records of receipts and expenditures, feed consumption, crop yields, and similar data are kept by each farmer individually. Standardized forms are used so the data from the different farms will be comparable.

The farm management specialist checks over the records to make sure they are complete. At the end of the year he supervises the process of summarization and analysis, usually employing an office helper for the purpose. Each farmer then receives his own records completely summarized, and also the averages from other farms of the same size and type in the group, for purposes of comparison. The specialist goes over these reports with the farmer, pointing out which enterprises have done well and

Fig. 62.—Advice from the fieldman on the coöperative farm management route.

which poorly. The next step is to plan how to bring the poor enterprises up to a satisfactory standard of performance.

The specialist should visit each farm once every two or three months. On this visit he checks up the farmer's records and talks with him about his management problems. He should be thoroughly acquainted with the farming conditions of the neighborhood and the methods best adapted to them. Because of this knowledge he may discover some problem of crop production, livestock feeding, or sanitation which the farmer himself has not yet noticed. In this case, he should point out the problem to the farmer as well as some suitable way of meeting it.

The route man can also help the coöperating farmers by giving them information about farm prices and the agricultural outlook. He helps them map their farms and compute crop yields, and since he is constantly traveling about among his coöperators, he knows where the farmer can find good breeding animals or high-yielding strains of seed.

This sort of service may add considerably to the farmer's net income. For satisfactory service, however, the specialist must be an extremely capable man, thoroughly trained both in farm management and in the technical methods of agriculture. He should be highly intelligent in order to size up the special problems of each of one to two hundred farmers. He should be genuinely interested in the success of his coöperators, and must have a sympathetic understanding of their viewpoints in order to gain and keep their confidence in his suggestions.

Men with these qualifications are hard to find. When a satisfactory farm management specialist is located for a position, the coöperators should realize that they have the services of a valuable and high-priced man and should not begrudge him a salary comparable to what he could earn elsewhere.

Other Coöperative Farm Management Methods

Various other means of coöperation are related directly or indirectly to the management of the farm. Coöperative purchases of feed or fertilizer may make worth-while savings in districts where large quantities of these materials are bought. Coöperative marketing may not be exactly part of the management of a farm, but at least the time which would be spent in looking for a market may be spent on the farm. No doubt there are still other services which farmers could profitably obtain on a coöperative basis. There are really a surprising number of ways in which farmers coöperate. We have mentioned the trading of labor, coöperative ownership of equipment, coöperative ownership of breeding stock, cow-testing associations, and farm-accounting associations. Each of these can provide the farmer with services he could not perform himself. Not only is it profitable for the farmer to learn to coöperate with his neighbors, but such coöperation also makes farm life much more enjoyable.

CHAPTER XXIV

Financing the Farm Business

The Problem: How can farm finances be organized to provide maximum safety and yet permit the farmer to pay off his debts as quickly and conveniently as possible? Where and on what terms should necessary funds be obtained?

Importance of Good Financial Organization

One farmer may be making steady progress toward paying off his debt and gaining financial independence, while his neighbor with a similar obligation alternates between periods of flush income and others of financial stress and worry. They may be equally good farmers and on equally good land. How has the first man organized his finances to avoid the troubles that beset his neighbor?

What is meant by "financial organization"? We may consider it here to refer to the proportions of funds for long or short time investment in the business, and the arrangements which have been made for obtaining them. We may think then that the most satisfactory plan would be to use only one's own funds and avoid any debt at all. The term "debt" carries with it many unpleasant associations and to some people is almost the equivalent of disgrace. Certainly the farmer who owns outright his farm and all his equipment and livestock is in a much more agreeable situation than one who is loaded down with a heavy debt burden.

Buying a farm requires a large investment. A quarter section farm at $100 per acre requires $16,000 for land and buildings alone. Then it is necessary to invest, perhaps, $1,500 in livestock and another $1,000 or so in equipment. Feeds, seed, and other supplies plus cash for current expenses will probably require another $1,000, to make about $20,000 in all. Where is the farmer to get this money? He might rent a farm and save what he earns, investing it in bonds or other conservative securities until he has amassed this sum. By this method farm ownership would be delayed many years. If the man is a good farmer and the price of land not too high in relation to its annual earnings, these funds should yield as much in a farm under his own care as they would in other types of investment. It would be a source of considerable satisfaction, besides, to be operating and perhaps improving his own farm.

If the farmer follows this second plan, he will probably operate a rented farm until he has saved what he regards as a safe margin on the price of a farm of his own. Then he will look for a source of credit from which he can borrow the remainder. He will have important arrangements to make with bankers, government loan agencies, private lenders, or insurance companies in borrowing this credit. The farmer should organize his business and meet his obligations in such a way that he will gain from the use of this credit.

When Is It Profitable to Borrow?

Farmers may want to borrow money for various reasons. Some of these are quite proper and profitable,

TABLE XLIX

BALANCE SHEET OF A 165 ACRE GRAIN FARM, JAN. 1, 1934

ASSETS

Liquid Assets:

Cattle, Young and Fattening Stock.............. $	317	
Hogs...	298	
Poultry......................................	110	
Feeds..	537	
Seeds and Supplies...........................	85	
Total Liquid Assets........................		$ 1,347

Working Assets:

Cattle, Breeding Stock........................	538	
Horses.......................................	480	
Tractor......................................	153	
Equipment...................................	718	
Auto (Farm share)............................	120	
Total Working Assets.......................		2,009

Fixed Assets:

Land...	14,665	
Buildings and Improvements...................	3,910	
Total Fixed Assets.........................		18,575
Total Assets..........................		21,931

LIABILITIES

Mortgage...	6,500	
Intermediate or long period notes..................	800	
Short time notes.................................	1,150	
Bills outstanding.................................	325	
Total Liabilities..............................		8,775
Net Worth..................................		13,156
		21,931

Net Capital Ratio 1 : 2.2
Working Ratio   1 : 1.5
Current Ratio   1 : 0.9

others may simply show that. the borrower is either a poor business man or is generally incompetent. In general, we might say that *borrowing is justified whenever the purpose for which the funds are to be used promises to return more than enough to repay the loan together with the interest.* If the purpose of the loan has little likelihood of yielding a profit over its cost, borrowing is undesirable.

Some funds are borrowed to buy things to be used by the family without yielding any economic returns. What should be the policy toward these? If the borrower desires a radio or new automobile so much that he is willing to pay the interest charges as the price of enjoying them and is sure he will have funds to pay off the loan when it falls due, there is no reason why he should not make the purchase. He should realize that this purchase is entirely different from his business operations and is to be justified on quite different grounds. Here we are concerned with business or productive loans and not with borrowing to buy consumer's goods.

There is nothing dishonorable about the use of credit, nor is there any reason for a farmer's regarding the village banker as some superior sort of being. The farmer should realize that he is paying for the service he is getting and that his only obligation to his creditor is his financial one. When he has given good security, has agreed to pay the interest and installments, and is meeting his obligations promptly, he is living up to his end of the bargain. The fact that he has borrowed the use of some other person's credit is nothing that should affect his self-respect.

Comparing the cost of a loan with the returns. A farmer is considering the purchase of a grain binder cost-

ing $250.   While he can hire one from a neighbor, having
his own binder will allow him to cut his grain at just
the right time and would also save the cost of hiring
the machine.   How shall he decide if he ought to borrow
the funds?   The answer will be determined by the total

Courtesy Farm Credit Administration.

Fig. 63.—A farmer pays off his loan to the secretary of the Production Credit Association after the crop is sold.

cost of owning and using the binder on the one hand,
compared with the cost of hiring on the other.   To the
latter should be added any increase in return from getting
the crop harvested in better season.

The loss of grain from late harvesting, we will suppose,
has been amounting to about $25 per year, and the cost
of hiring the binder has been $30.   This makes the total
saving from owning a machine about $55 per year.   What
are the costs to be balanced against this?

Repairs on the machine the farmer estimates at about $10 per year. The machine will probably last ten years. With a purchase price of $250 a charge of $25 per year for depreciation will be necessary. That is, it should be possible to set aside this sum each year from the earnings of the machine to create a fund for its replacement. Interest must also be considered. If the money is borrowed, interest will have to be paid. If the farmer buys the binder with his own funds, he is giving up the opportunity to invest the money somewhere else where it would earn interest for him.

The charge for interest should not be computed on the entire purchase price for the whole life of the machine. The purchase price is $250, but by the end of the first year it has depreciated by $25. The value of the binder then at the beginning of the second year is $225, at the third year $200 and so on to the beginning of the tenth year, when it is worth $25. If depreciation proceeds in a straight line, as has been assumed in this example, the average interest for the entire life of the machine may be found by multiplying half the purchase price by the interest rate. Computed at 6 per cent on $125, this would give the average interest charge of $7.50.

Adding depreciation and interest to the annual repair bill gives a total of $42.50, which represents the average annual cost of using the binder. Since this is definitely less than the estimated saving of $55, it would pay the farmer to buy the machine.

If there had been only a narrow margin in favor of buying the machine, an increase to 7 or 8 per cent in the interest rate might make the purchase unprofitable. In this case, however, it would require an interest rate of about 16 per cent to consume all the advantage as long as repairs and depreciation remain as given. A change of one or two per cent may sometimes make other types of investment, as well, unprofitable. Opportunity cost should also be considered. If the farmer's funds are limited, he may find it more advantageous to choose something else in which to invest them.

Paying the interest may be easier than paying off the loan. In such a case as this, the repayment or replacement of the principal (i.e., the depreciation charge) amounts to considerably more than the annual charge for interest. But all the elements of cost should be considered together before the decision is made to borrow the funds. The farmer often considers only the interest rate when borrowing for short-lived equipment, whereas repayment of the principal is really the more difficult part. The few dollars of interest are relatively easy to raise. The longer the life of the asset, the less important becomes the depreciation and the more important the rate of interest.

Additional capital can be generally used in many ways on a farm. The question is which of those uses would repay the loans and the necessary expenses for interest and upkeep. The farmer who borrows funds only when he is reasonably sure that the purposes in which he invests them will yield more than the added expense is making a businesslike and profitable use of credit. The man who borrows carelessly without weighing benefits against costs of the loan soon finds himself with a growing and fruitless burden.

Overborrowing to buy land. Overborrowing to purchase land has been common in recent years. An expected increase in the resale value of land or other asset justifies paying a higher price for it. But if speculative buying leads a farmer to pay a decided premium, he may find himself paying out most of his current earnings in order to keep his claim to the expected increase. Suppose that a farm costing $100 per acre may be rented out for $5 per acre above the current expenses for upkeep and taxes. The farmer has enough money saved to be able to pay down $40 per acre, and must borrow the remaining $60 at 5 per cent. At this rate the farm will yield 5 per cent interest on his own funds and just pay the interest on the $60 he borrowed.

Suppose a large increase in land prices is expected and people are bidding the land up to $140. This means the farmer would have to borrow $100 instead of $60. The $5 return per acre would then merely cover interest on the borrowed $100 and bring no returns on the $40 the farmer invested.

An even less favorable situation is possible. Let us suppose that the land was bought for $180, of which $40 was still the farmer's own money. At 5 per cent he has obligated himself to pay $7 per acre interest each year. Since the land is capable of earning only $5, he can expect no return on his own $40 and will have to pay the additional $2 interest from the earnings of his labor and management or else lose the farm. On the basis of its earnings the land in the last two cases has been over-valued, unless a very decided increase in price actually occurs. The farmer in the second case, and certainly in the third, has overborrowed; that is, he has borrowed more than the farm is able to repay with interest.

Type of Assets as Related to Type of Loans

The loan obtained should correspond to the type of asset for which it is to be used. A farmer who wants to buy additional land has part of the necessary money and his credit is good. He could give a note for a year for the borrowed money. Would this be a desirable arrangement? Another farmer who wants to buy more equipment and livestock finds that the cheapest funds are available on long-time mortgages. Should he take advantage of this lower cost and mortgage his farm to buy equipment?

The rate of turnover on investment in land is very slow. The total rent would probably not exceed seven or eight per cent on the investment if the land were rented out. It should earn at about the same rate if operated by the owner. After taxes and upkeep expenses are paid, it is likely that not more than five or six per cent will remain as earnings on the investment. It would take a good many years for the land to pay for itself if it earned six per cent while the interest rate on the borrowed money was five per cent. The length of the loan should be accordingly long. A two or three year mortgage would have to be renewed many times, with considerable trouble and perhaps added cost as commission.

Suppose the farmer bought livestock and equipment with money from a long-term mortgage. Here the rate of turnover on these short-lived assets is much more rapid. Part of the returns from their use should be used each year to pay off the loan. If these annual payments are too small, the farmer will find himself still owing money on worn-out equipment, or he will be "paying for a dead horse." The tendency of most people is to pay only what is required each year on large obligations and use the rest of the funds for current purposes. In general, it is a good policy to arrange payments to conform to the earnings of the asset purchased with them.

Desirable Characteristics of a Loan

The term of the loan should generally not exceed the probable life of the asset which is to be purchased. If the loan is for the purchase of feed for hogs, it should be arranged to be paid off when the hogs are sold. For

Courtesy Farm Credit Association

Fig. 64.—Annual meeting of a farm credit association.

equipment, however, it would hardly be desirable to continue the loan for the life of the machine. In this case the better policy is to repay part of the loan with each crop raised for a period of two or three years. If long-time loans are made on equipment, the machines are depreciating, and unless payments are kept up the security back of the loan is becoming poorer and poorer.

A second general rule is, *the contract for the loan*

should not require repayment faster than the rate of earning of the purchased asset will permit. If a note of $100 for the purchase of a mowing machine is the only debt a farmer has, it would of course be foolish to prolong this debt for two or three years. In purchasing a larger asset, such as land or buildings, the contract should not require annual payments greater than the probable yearly earnings.

A third rule is that *the contract should permit paying off the principal faster than the scheduled payments whenever the farmer has extra funds available.* The borrower would find it very annoying if the lender refused to accept payment until the end of the period set by the mortgage. This point is usually covered by a clause in the mortgage or contract which allows the borrower to make extra payments on the principal at any date when interest is due.

Fourth, on long-time loans, such as those used in buying land, *regular amortization payments should be provided for on the principal.* In this way current payments consist of interest plus a small payment on the principal. A uniform payment is made each year, but the size of the payment applying on the principal is constantly increasing. For example, if the interest rate is $5\frac{1}{2}$ per cent, payments of $6\frac{1}{2}$ per cent per year in semiannual installments will pay off the debt in $34\frac{1}{2}$ years. If amortization is not provided for, the farmer is apt to postpone making payments on the principal from year to year, allowing the debt to become practically a permanent one.

A fifth requirement is that *the interest rate should be as low as the money market permits.* The farmer should investigate all possible sources of funds in order to get the lowest rate.

Variations in Interest

Interest rates, however, may properly vary with the risk incurred and the type of security offered. The greater the risk the lender thinks there may be of losing the principal, the higher the rate must be to induce him to make the loan. Farmers who have a reputation of being careless and irresponsible in their dealings with lenders, so that the latter are often put to the expense and trouble of legal action to secure payment, may find they either cannot get a loan or must pay a high rate of interest.

The size of the loan also affects the rate. It is much cheaper for the lender to administer and collect a mortgage of $5,000 than fifty loans of $100 each. If small loans are to be as profitable as mortgages, the interest rate must be higher to offset the extra expense of bookkeeping and administration.

The type of security offered for the loan will have some influence both on the rate and on the willingness of the lender to extend the credit. The farmer who offers a government bond for security can expect the banker to be more willing to make the loan than he would be to a man who offers a chattel mortgage on his farm machinery. The bond could easily and quickly be sold if the farmer failed to meet his obligation, but there would be much more trouble and expense, as well as uncertainty, involved in disposing of the farm machinery. No banker likes to foreclose, but the borrower should remember that the bank has obligations to its depositors which are just as binding as the borrower's obligations to the bank.

Planning to Meet Obligations

The farmer, or any other person who is operating partly on borrowed capital, should adopt a definite budget or plan for meeting and retiring his obligations. The slipshod debtor makes life unnecessarily hard for himself. Without planning ahead for payments on his obligations, he is almost certain to be embarrassed every time a note or mortgage comes due. As the date of maturity approaches, he should make an effort to put aside sufficient funds to meet interest charges and to pay off at least part of the principal of each note.

Farm accounts, which have been summarized by months, will help greatly in making up this financial budget. The schedule of payments should correspond with the regular dates of farm receipts and should be a part of the regular farm budget. This schedule should provide for retiring obligations as rapidly as convenient, but it should not be too ambitious. Even the payment of debts can be made more burdensome than it need be.

What is a Satisfactory Financial Organization?

Every farm business has a fairly definite financial organization, whether the farmer realizes it or not. He should realize just where his finances stand so that he can exercise the greatest possible control over them.

The assets of the business may be classified as fixed, working, and current. The fixed assets include land, buildings, fences, drains, and other resources which are practically permanent in character. Working assets are such things as machinery, work stock, and breeding stock. These are things which last more than one year and usually have a productive life of less than ten or fifteen years. It is of course difficult to set any exact limit. The third group includes such things as crops on hand, seeds, feeds, and fattening livestock, which are normally turned into cash by the end of the current year.

Liabilities may be divided into three similar groups. First is the long-time indebtedness usually in the form of real-estate mortgages, which require a series of payments over a period of years. The payment is either postponed to a later date or is being retired in small amounts each year through amortization. These mortgages usually represent the purchase price of the land or its permanent improvements. The credit may be obtained from a Federal Land Bank, from insurance companies, or from private individuals.

Other liabilities are in the form of short-term notes or floating bills. The credit obtained with these was probably used to buy fertilizers, feeds, or other supplies, to purchase feeding stock, or to hire labor. These obligations are to mature before the end of the current year, probably within six months. Commercial banks are not usually permitted to make loans for longer periods. They will therefore have to be paid out of income received during the current year. These obligations may either represent funds borrowed from the bank or from private individuals or simply unpaid balances of bills.

Notes are often made out for a period of three months with the understanding that only a partial payment is to be made at the end of that period and that they are then to be renewed. Such notes may run one or two years in this manner, although they are in the form of current obligations, and the holder can demand their payment at any renewal date. This is an unsatisfactory method of financing, because the farmer can never tell in advance just when the lender will insist upon payment. The farmer who has several notes of this type outstanding has really turned the control of his financial system over to the changing whims of his creditors.

Ratios of Liabilities to Assets

What is a safe ratio between the various types of assets and liabilities? To indicate the safety of the entire business, the *net capital ratio* is used. This is the ratio of total liabilities to total assets, and a ratio of at least 1:2 is regarded as desirable. The net capital ratio in Table XLIX, for example, is 1:2.2, which indicates a fairly safe financial situation. That is to say, if this farmer sold out his entire business and paid off all his debts, he would have over half the price of his business left for himself.

The *working capital ratio* is used to indicate the intermediate financial situation. This is the ratio between intermediate and current liabilities on the one side and working and liquid assets on the other. The farmer whose figures are shown in Table XLIX is in poorer financial condition with regard to the intermediate than the long-time period, since his working ratio is only 1:1.5. In other words he would have to sell two-thirds of his liquid and working assets to pay off his intermediate obligations. Or a decline of one-third in the price level of those assets would wipe out his margin of safety.

His *current ratio* (the ratio between current liabilities and liquid assets) is even more unsatisfactory. This ratio is only 1:0.9. If creditors holding the notes and floating bills were to press for payment, he would be unable to meet their claims even if he sold all his liquid assets.

The condition of the business as a whole in this case is satisfactory, but the situation with regard to shorter time obligations is precarious. The farmer should have obtained a larger mortgage loan and kept his short-term loans smaller. The value of the land is sufficient to carry a mortgage of about $8,750 at the 1:2 ratio. This would have deferred all but about $1,000 of his debt until a later period, or better still, would have permitted him to make small regular payments on the long-time loan while paying off the $1,000 of short-term debt. If a large amount of credit is to be borrowed, it is advisable, both for safety and for the farmer's peace of mind, that as much of it as possible be in a long-time form. The farmer can still pay off his debt as fast as possible, and with this sort of financial organization he has greater freedom and safety in his short-time operations.

References

Lee, Virgil P., *Principles of Agricultural Credit*, McGraw-Hill, New York, 1930.

Farm Credit Administration, *First Annual Report*, 1933.

Iowa Bulletin 315: "Farm Mortgage Policy," by William G. Murray, 1934.

Minnesota *Farmers' Institute Annual*, Number 29, 1916.

Information regarding conditions and methods of obtaining loans may be obtained by writing to the Farm Credit Administration, Washington, D. C., or by writing to the Federal Farm Land Banks or Production Credit Corporations at Springfield, Mass.; Baltimore, Md.; Columbia, S. C.; Louisville, Ky.; New Orleans, La.; St. Louis, Mo.; St. Paul, Minn.; Omaha, Nebr.; Wichita, Kans.; Houston, Texas; Berkeley, Calif., or Spokane, Wash.

CHAPTER XXV

The Farmer's Market Contacts

The Problem: How shall the farmer adjust his economic organization to the business world? How can he purchase supplies most economically? How can he dispose of his products for maximum prices?

Farm Production Should be Adjusted to the Market

The farmer often thinks he fails to get proper returns because of an inefficient marketing system, or because there is too great a spread between the producer and the consumer. He complains that he loses in both directions because he sells at wholesale and buys at retail. The implication is that if the marketing system were reorganized he might get a larger part of the retail prices when he sells and also save part of his expenses by buying at wholesale.

Certainly marketing contacts play an important part in determining the farmer's financial success. One important question, however, should be raised at the beginning of the discussion. Shall we attempt to adjust the market to the producing habits of the farmer or to adjust the production of the farmer to the market? Many farmers, particularly if they have not had much contact with the retail sale of their own products, are likely to feel that their products are necessities and that it is up to the market to pay them satisfactory prices

368

for the things they produce. The consumer in the city, on the other hand, is apt to have a different point of view. Why, he asks, should he pay high prices for things he doesn't want or for things that are being produced in too large a volume?

Both sides are likely to agree, however, when figures are presented to show that the consumer is paying nearly twice as much as the farmer receives for milk, fresh vegetables, meat, and other farm products. Both farmer and consumer will probably conclude offhand that the spread is excessive, and there must be some sort of "racket" that is taking an excessive toll in the marketing process.

What should be the attitude of the farmer toward the market? He is likely to find that there are relatively few things that he as an individual can do to change marketing practices or market prices. Consumers have developed fairly definite wants and are willing to pay for their satisfaction. The farmer or other business man who produces things that are wanted will find a ready market, but will have a hard time finding anyone willing to pay for something relatively unwanted.

The price at which a product can be sold depends on the intensity of desire for the quantity that is offered for sale. The first problem of a groceryman opening a new store is to find out what articles his prospective customers are willing to buy at prices which will make it profitable to handle them. The farm implement dealer who insisted in laying in a stock of surreys or ox yokes would not last long. Nor would the farmer who insists on selling his steers at an age of four years and weighing a ton, even though this was the popular weight a few decades ago. The person who wants to make a business success will find it profitable to study the wants of the market.

This does not mean that the farmer should turn over his product to the first marketing agency that happens along. If he becomes familiar with various marketing agencies, he may be able to sell his goods at better prices than some of his neighbors. The point is, however, that the farm needs to be adjusted to the marketing situation as it exists—or rather as it appears likely to exist when the produce will be ready for sale.

Buying for the Farm

The farmer has also the problem of buying. With regard to city-made products, this problem is about the same as that of the city consumer and farm produce. The farmer needs a supply of feeds, fertilizers, equipment, fuel, and household supplies. It is seldom necessary that he purchase any particular brand or make. The type or brand of feed, for example, most satisfactory from a business standpoint depends both on physical characteristics and also on its relative price.

It nearly always pays to plan ahead for necessary supplies and to decide when, where, and how to purchase. No general rule can be given. The most profitable practice will depend on the nature of the article, on the type of dealer by whom it is handled, on the price outlook, and on the individual farmer's situation.

Feed or fertilizer should be bought long enough in advance to be available just when needed. If there is a definite reason for expecting a price rise, it would pay to obtain the supply before the rise begins. This may depend on the situation of that particular farmer. If he has no adequate storage facilities, the advantages of early buying may be offset by heavy spoilage. Funds for the purchase may not be available in time to buy most profitably. This suggests another important advantage of a well-planned financial organization, as discussed in the last chapter.

If a farmer expects to save by buying in large quantities, he should weigh against the saving in price the cost of the capital which he must tie up. If he has to borrow the funds, this will usually be quite clear to him. There are also insurance costs and perhaps additional handling costs. This latter expense is not always necessary, because it is often possible to haul the feed or fertilizer at a slack time or on return trips. To make a worth-while saving the farm should be equipped to handle and store the supply so as to avoid wastage or spoilage.

Coöperative purchasing. Buying wholesale lots of feeds, fertilizers, spray materials, and so on, is another possible means of saving. A large dairy farmer may save considerably by buying carlots of such supplies as cottonseed meal or bran, while a small farmer must buy a ton or even a few sacks at a time.

The small farmer can obtain most of the advantages of wholesale purchasing by coöperation with his neighbors. In some parts of the country there are well-established coöperative purchasing organizations. These may be set up for that particular purpose or they may be operated jointly with coöperative elevators or creameries. They may offer opportunities for worth-while saving. A common weakness is that these organizations may be too lenient in collecting from farmers. In the long run the expense of carrying this credit is borne by the farmers who do pay their bills promptly. Another difficulty is that they sometimes try to operate on so narrow a margin that they are forced out of business. The farmer should not expect to buy from coöperatives for wholesale prices. He is really demanding the services of retailing and these are expensive to perform.

Choosing the Time to Sell

Deciding when to sell a crop is one of the farmer's problems. This crop may be one that has been harvested and is ready to sell, or the decision may be between feeding a lot of hogs or cattle longer or selling at once. His problem may be concerned with an entire production process and may involve planning several months in advance of the market.

If corn or wheat is being held for sale, he must compare the probable price movement during the next few months with costs of storage. The price outlook must first be analyzed. Sometimes there are definite reasons for expecting a decided rise or fall in price. Large or small crops about to be harvested, the number of hogs or cattle on feed, and probable improvements in business activity should all be considered.

The usual seasonal movement of price is one of the most dependable factors. Some of the more common of these seasonal movements are shown in Fig. 65. Prices of crops usually reach their seasonal low point just after harvest, then rise to a peak shortly before the next harvest. Large or small crops of grain cause different price movements. After a small crop the price fails to reach as low a level after harvest and then rises less than usual. After large harvests, prices drop sharply followed by a more pronounced rise during the winter and spring. The usual seasonal rise is roughly equal to the cost of storage plus interest on the value of crop plus loss by shrinkage.

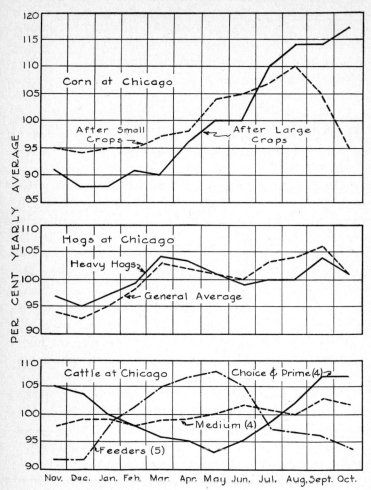

Fig. 65.—Seasonal variations in prices of farm products.

Corn prices from Iowa Circular 113.

Hog price data furnished by Prof. G. S. Shepherd, Iowa Agricultural Experiment Station.

Cattle prices from Iowa Research Bulletin 101 and U. S. Department of Agriculture, Bureau of Agricultural Economics.

The price, of course, does not often follow the exact path shown in Fig. 65.

The farmer should consider these usual or normal price movements as well as his facilities for storing the grain crop. Following a short corn crop, Fig. 65 suggests that there will seldom be a profit in holding. After a large crop, holding is much more likely to be profitable, provided the farm has weather-proof and pest-proof storage facilities.

Feeding livestock for the high market. In livestock feeding an additional factor is involved. As hogs or cattle become heavier, putting on added weight is more expensive. If a crop of fall pigs is about ready for market in June, for example, the cost of feeding them two weeks longer is likely to offset the profit from the higher price. In the first place, the higher price may not actually arrive. Also, considerable feed will be necessary to keep them, even if the rise does occur. There is also risk of losses by death. If a feeding period is to be prolonged without seriously added cost, the plans should be changed at the earliest possible date and before the stock becomes very fat. In the fall, hogs should be sold as early as possible, since the price ordinarily declines 12 or 14 per cent from September to December. Here cost increases and price falls the longer the hogs are kept.

A marketing date may be chosen by timing the entire production process so that the hogs or cattle would normally be ready to sell in the month desired. Fig. 65 shows that hogs are usually from 12 to 14 per cent higher in August and September than in December. Fat cattle are usually 7 or 8 per cent higher in August and September than in February or March. Feeder cattle are usually highest in April and May, because in these months pasture is just becoming available and there is a strong demand for livestock to utilize it.

The farmer who plans to take advantage of higher prices by having his hogs ready for market in September should also consider the greater difficulty in getting hogs to marketable weights by this time. The most

Courtesy Chicago Stockyards Co.
Fig. 66.—The Chicago Stockyards.

skillful hog raisers can usually do this, particularly if they have warm hog houses where their pigs can be far-rowed in February or March. Where the hog house and equipment are poor, it may not be feasible to farrow in the earlier months. Even with satisfactory equipment, not many farmers find that they can get their hogs to marketable weights before October or November, and the heaviest market movement is in December and January.

With cattle feeding there are similar problems of the cost of making the high-priced market. If cattle are to be fed for five or six months, they should be put on feed in April or May to make the August-September markets. Feeder cattle would then have to be bought when they are highest in April or May, or else roughed through the winter and then put on feed in the spring. While this latter method permits feeding up the corn stalks and other roughage during the winter, it also requires valuable time to feed the cattle during the busy crop-growing season. This might be profitable for the large commercial feeder to whom crops are a relatively minor matter, but not for the small feeder to whom crop production is as important as feeding.

The time of marketing is well worth considering, but the plans should be made as far in advance of the market as possible. The marketing plans must, by all means, be made to fit the plan of farm operation, or the gain in price may be lost elsewhere.

Selecting the Market

Selection of the market in which the product is to be sold is another important problem. A market that wants the type of product that the particular farm produces should naturally be chosen. There are many examples of differences in market preferences. The New York market, for example, prefers white eggs, while Boston prefers brown eggs. New York takes blanched asparagus, while the Boston market likes it green. Various conditions in the marketing of hogs have led to typical differences in weights and types. In the Middle Atlantic states hogs are ordinarily sold at 150 to 175 pounds, while in the Middle West they are marketed at 200 to 220 pounds. Certain packers have also developed special outlets for their products. One may have an outlet for light pigs, while another has developed a method of disposing of heavy hogs and sows. The farmer should become acquainted with the preferences of several potential markets to which he could sell his products. He may find a better outlet for the livestock or other produce he is raising, or he may uncover a profitable demand for a new type which he could produce to advantage.

The farmer should also find out if the price in his usual market is temporarily out of line with that in another accessible outlet. Irregular marketing of perishable products may lead to occasional gluts in a particular market. In order to avoid these, the farmer should check up on his usual market before shipping.

There are also seasonal variations in spreads between markets. For a period of two or three months one interior packing plant may pay 10 or 20 cents above its usual differential with Chicago prices for a particular weight of hogs. The price on light hogs, for example, may run further above heavy hogs during the summer months in one market than in another. Even though these differences may seem small, 25 cents a hundred pounds means $40 per car, and obtaining this is worth some trouble.

Choosing a Marketing Method

After deciding when and where to sell, the next question is *how* to sell—by what method. Shall the farmer consign his crops to a commission merchant and let him find a buyer? Should he sell to a local livestock or grain dealer, or perhaps to a buyer for a packing house? Or should he join a coöperative marketing agency and have the manager sell his stock along with that of his neighbors?

If the commodity requires personal inspection by the buyer, as in the case of ungraded grain or fruit, a sale through a commission merchant, who knows the market demands, may be the most profitable. This may also be true if the farmer is not himself acquainted with the marketing machinery.

If the market fluctuates widely, it may be advisable to sell to a buyer for a packing firm or even to a local dealer. In this way the farmer avoids a chance of a drop in price while the product is in transit. In the case of livestock he would also avoid yardage, feed, and other expenses in the central stockyards. He should be sure, however, that the price he is offered is as high as he would net through the public market at the time of sale.

The coöperative association provides another means of selling. Presumably it is conducted by an experienced manager, who should be able to find the best market and to get the produce to it as economically as possible. If the manager is not alert and experienced, he may get no better returns for the livestock or grain than the farmer could get himself. In this case the only advantage would be the saving of the farmer's time.

Functions of Coöperative Marketing

Important advantages are often gained by coöperative marketing, but this is not necessarily the case. The principles of marketing are outside the scope of this book, but it is worth while enumerating some of the principal purposes of coöperative marketing operations. It was mentioned in the paragraph above that a coöperative selling agency can save the farmer the trouble of looking up his own markets. It may also perform the service better than he could do it himself without special training or experience.

Second, the coöperative marketing organization may be able to reduce the cost of marketing operations by performing the same function as the local dealer but at a lower cost. Clark and Weld enumerate the following eight functions of the wholesale middleman:

1. To establish connections with country shippers (or with farmers who have produce to ship).
2. To provide facilities for storing and handling goods.
3. To sort, grade, and repack the produce and prepare it for market.
4. To study the needs of the retail trade and establish connection with retailers. (This is a function seldom undertaken by coöperatives unless the product is one which is distributed to retailers in the same form as when it leaves the farm.)
5. To deliver to retail stores from day to day in the quantities wanted.
6. To finance country shippers and retail stores.
7. To regulate the flow of the commodity among the various markets, and thereby prevent gluts and obtain the greatest return from the stock sold.
8. To furnish the machinery for accounting for the huge volume of goods handled.

The coöperative may regulate the flow of produce between markets so that there will not be losses from gluts in some while others are under-supplied. If the coöperative agency handles a large part of the crop, the flow of commodities may be regulated more evenly over the year. In the case of some agricultural products, notably citrus fruits, this has led to a widening of the marketing season and the sale of a larger volume than would have been possible a decade or two ago at the same price level.

Another opportunity is in preventing any avoidable shrinkage or waste and in providing the best and most economical care for perishable products. If the commodity is adapted to grading, returns may be increased by providing the consumer at all times with a uniform

Fig. 67.—A coöperative creamery.

and dependable grade of product. The product may also be made more attractive to the consumer by more pleasing or convenient packaging.

Economy in marketing is made possible by handling a large volume of produce and by maintaining this volume over the greater part of the year. Sometimes it is possible to save transportation and handling expense either by closer sorting to avoid shipping low-grade fruits or vegetables or by converting low-grade products into others of a higher value per unit of weight or bulk.

Each product, of course, presents a marketing problem

of its own. The functions of economical marketing can in some cases be handled as well by the private dealer as by the coöperative. In other cases a high degree of coöperation with the growers themselves is needed for the best results. Large coöperatives have shown themselves very valuable in bringing about more regular marketing, at least when the nature of the product and of the market favored them.

Coöperative Marketing and Price

Many people think that a coöperative marketing organization, in order to be successful, should include all or nearly all of the producers of the crop it is to handle. In this way they think it would be possible to obtain higher prices. In other words, their idea is that the primary purpose of coöperative organization is to permit price manipulation or to obtain a monopoly advantage.

Nevertheless, the sellers, no matter how highly organized, cannot by themselves determine prices. The demand side of the market is just as important as the supply. Of course it is possible to sell apples, for example, at a higher price than the free competitive level. But the higher price means that a smaller amount will be sold. The monopolist is able to obtain the price he asks only because he keeps a rigid control over supply. If an organization of farmers were to establish a monopoly over the sale of apples or potatoes (a thing which they have not yet been able to do with any important product) they would have to limit their production as well as control their sales. Even if such an organization were possible it would have certain disadvantages.

First, the gain from the higher price might be small or wholly lacking. If the monopoly were over the production of such commodities as potatoes or wheat, which people habitually consume in relatively fixed amounts, a ten per cent reduction in supply would probably permit selling the crop for a price 15 or 18 per cent higher. Selling 90 per cent of a normal crop for 115 per cent of the normal price would yield 103.5 per cent of the normal income. This would increase the total income by 3.5 per cent if there were no expenses connected with the crop limitation program.

Higher prices may not pay. The demand for products which are of the luxury or semi-luxury type, such as mushrooms or strawberries, is more elastic. That is, the amount demanded by consumers varies more widely than the price. In such a case a ten per cent crop reduction might permit only a five per cent rise in price. Selling a 90 per cent crop for 105 per cent of the usual price would bring in only 94.5 per cent of the normal income. In other words, the total income of growers might actually be reduced by the crop reduction program.

A second pitfall in the way of any attempted monopoly is that, if the organization should actually be successful in raising the price of the product, it would be profitable for new growers to take advantage of the efforts of the organization. In several cases where combinations of producers have been able to reduce their own output, the benefits have gone to outsiders. The organization in such cases soon finds itself producing a part instead of the whole crop.

A third difficulty in the way of monopoly is that consumers have much more effective ways of protecting themselves than is commonly realized. If the price of apples, for example, were appreciably raised and kept at a high level for two or three years, the consuming habits of the public would probably change. If the price of all fruits were raised, people would soon substitute more vegetables in place of fruit, and would make a more economical use of the fruits they did buy.

Coöperative marketing agencies, in short, are likely to find plenty of useful and profitable work to do in saving unnecessary costs of marketing, grading, and standardizing their product and bringing about a more regular flow to market. All of these tend to increase the net return to the producer without setting destructive forces into operation. Monopoly and artificial manipulation of prices are much more difficult to accomplish than is usually supposed, and even if successful, such efforts may result in little or no net gain.

References

Clark, Fred E., and Weld, L. D. H., *Marketing Agricultural Products in the United States,* Macmillan, New York, 1932.

Nourse, E. G., and Knapp, Joseph G., *The Coöperative Marketing of Livestock,* The Brookings Institution, Washington, D. C., 1931.

Index